LOVE TO SLEEP

EVE SQUIRES
and GEMMA FRYER

LOVE TO SLEEP

Good nights and happy days
for your child and you

First published in Great Britain in 2022 by Orion Spring
an imprint of The Orion Publishing Group Ltd
Carmelite House, 50 Victoria Embankment
London EC4Y 0DZ

An Hachette UK Company

1 3 5 7 9 10 8 6 4 2

A CIP catalogue record for this book is
available from the British Library.

ISBN (Trade Paperback) 978 1 3987 0266 0
ISBN (eBook) 978 1 3987 0267 7
ISBN (Audio) 978 1 3987 0287 5

Typeset by www.carrdesignstudio.com
Printed in Great Britain by Clays Ltd, Elcograf S.p.A.

www.orionbooks.co.uk

To the ones we gave life to; who gave it right back.

For our children: Tilly, Finley, Toby, Sena, Louis, Ted, Kit and

Posie. May you always have the courage to show up in the

world as unapologetically you as possible.

CONTENTS

FOREWORD

Sleep was without doubt my biggest challenge as a child and it went on to become my greatest trial as a parent. I had a long childhood history of poor sleep, heavily reliant on my parents' presence to help me sleep. I experienced anxiety if ever I had to sleep without them or my brothers, and I didn't want that for my own children.

When I became a parent, I wanted to make sure my children didn't feel the way I had felt: alone and afraid at night unless my parents were there. I wanted them to feel more enabled, more safe and more secure than I did when it came to sleep.

My own children were two and four when we approached Calm & Bright to help us with sleep. My four year old, Lola, was having some night wakings. Rather unsurprisingly, she was whiny and irritable in the day as a result. Before the sleep teaching, Lola was often irrationally teary, the tears seeming to come from nowhere. Kit went the other way – he was more wired than weepy. He fought sleep at most turns; naps, bedtime, overnight and early wakes. At the peak, he was waking six to eight times a night! The impact on him was clear to see – Kit was so far beyond tired that at times he couldn't even walk without tripping over himself. It was hard to see. I felt helpless.

It wasn't just the children who were suffering with our family's lack of sleep. When I am tired I am irrational, irritable and angry. I go straight to burnout and my body makes it clear that I need to make a change. Alarm bells ring. I am unable to function clearly and lose my ability to remain patient and compassionate as a mother, wife, daughter, or friend, let alone have any energy left to take care of my own needs. (I've yet to meet an exhausted parent who can.)

Before I encountered Calm & Bright I would push through those signs, not knowing what to do or where to turn. I ploughed on, as so many of us do, believing that broken sleep was just part and parcel of being a parent. How wrong I was!

The very first time Eve and I spoke, I had a calm feeling that everything was going to be ok. I felt like I had finally been given the permission to go with my gut. That I had been heard. I felt empowered to discover that I had the ability to sort my sleep out myself. I just needed the right tools to do it. And that is precisely what I gained from working with Eve and Gem.

Within a surprisingly short period of time, both the children were finally getting the rest they needed, taking the full eleven to twelve solid hours of sleep a night that Eve said that they were capable of. They were settling more peacefully, waking later and noticeably calmer. It really was transformational for all the family.

When I tell you that Calm & Bright changed my life, I do it with my hand on my heart. If you are a parent who struggles with sleep, or if you are feeling anxiety surrounding it, this book is for you. Parenting is hard enough without showing up each day shattered. It is so important that parents know the help is out there. That there is another, new way.

This book will wave a magic wand of empowerment for shattered parents around the globe. It excites me greatly that Eve and Gem's message will finally be in the hands of the people who need it the most. Make good use of the words before you. Your future is in your hands with the help of these sleep angels!

Love,
Izzy x

INTRODUCTION

If you're reading these words, it may well be with weary eyes. If you are listening to them, perhaps your ears fell deaf to the promise of sleep long ago. Maybe you're so *beyond tired* that your back is breaking, your mind foggy, your energy zapped and your hope for a rested life fading. Maybe the idea of living a rested life is irritatingly laughable to you, more like a naff TV advert than something you can reach out and grasp. By now, you may be so used to broken sleep that you've come to believe that it's just the hand you've been dealt; that it's supposed to be exhausting and you just need to get a grip. Perhaps exhaustion has stripped you of optimism and hope so completely that you find talk of better sleep just bullshit. That even if it were possible, it's not going to happen for you because there's clearly something wrong with you or your baby. If you're not yet an exhausted parent, you might be an expectant one, keen to avoid any unnecessary sleep deprivation by gently laying down the foundations for healthy sleep right from the start. You may be reading this because you have deep reservations about sleep teaching because of the godawful things you've heard about it. Doesn't it flood the baby's brain with cortisol? Isn't it selfish? Doesn't it give your child the message that you won't come? That their needs don't matter? Doesn't it have a negative impact on their brain and body and relationships into adulthood? It's not even *possible* for babies to self-settle, is it? Whoever you are, and for whatever reason you are reading it, this book will liberate you. Within these pages you will discover the restrictive beliefs and behaviours that keep broken sleep cycles going years longer than they need to. We'll share with you the exact things that keep parents too tired for too long. You'll learn how to drown out the noise and do sleep *your* way, freeing you up to live your one life how you want to. You will be filled with such confidence in your ability to sort your child's sleep that you'll be able to navigate each age and stage with ease and curiosity, rather than fear and dread.

Imagine for a moment that we are handing you a piece of paper right now with the exact number of minutes, hours, days, weeks, months and possibly even years that you have been polluted by poor sleep. Now picture yourself during that time. Are you pacing the floor at a godawful time of night? Searching frantically online for answers? Shouting until you see their little lips wobble and then feeling immense guilt? Putting them in the car or pram with gritted teeth to force a nap? Holding on to them tighter when they hug you so that they don't see that you're crying? Wondering if you've lost it? Why you seem to struggle more than others? Why you just can't bloody well figure it out? Now imagine that time and energy focused elsewhere; on the people, places and things that matter most. Imagine that you're not only going to have that time back, you're going to be rested enough to enjoy it and really be *there* for it. Can you dare to see your future self now? Maybe she's pushing that swing with playfulness and sparkle rather than gritted teeth and glazed-over eyes. Maybe she feels good about herself and how she's mothering. Perhaps cooking food for her family gives her pleasure rather than a headache. Perhaps she is living with thanks and hope, with playfulness and presence. Perhaps even though life's shit sometimes, she's always able to reset each day with a good night's sleep. How does she feel? How does she look? What are her dreams? What is she capable of?

The crash

It all began twelve years ago when I crashed my car with my baby in it. My ten-month-old had never slept more than two hours at a time and was breastfeeding on newborn regularity despite being almost a toddler. Surviving on little to no sleep had taken a devastating toll on my physical and mental health. Exhaustion had left no stone unturned when it came to its effect on my body or mind. I was tired, yes, but it was more than that. Starved of sleep, my eyelids twitched in protest, and the bruises on my body spoke of how I bumped into doorways regularly as my brain failed to measure distances accurately. I felt breathless climbing the stairs and my arms ached when I folded laundry. I would forget and lose things regularly such as my keys and my phone (which was often in my hand all along). On more than one occasion, I lost a child for a few moments. Looking back, it was only a matter of time before something had to give.

The crash was the perfect catalyst for change I had no idea I so desperately needed. It left me with no choice but to sort sleep if I was to save my family from the hazardous path we were treading. Deep down, I knew that it wasn't meant to be this way and that it was time for me to take some action for change. Within three days of creating my own loving and responsive approach (as none of the ones I could find were gentle enough for me), my non-sleeping baby was sleeping twelve hours a night, every night. A few days on, I was elated but in shock. I couldn't get my head around the fact that twelve-hour nights of sleep (the stuff of every tired mum's dreams) had been just a few days away all along. I couldn't help but think about how different my and my daughter's experience of the first year would have been if only I'd have known there was another way.

As the twelve-hour nights (and two-hour naps) began to take hold, life was immeasurably brighter. Filled with an overwhelming sense of purpose, I felt compelled to help other shattered parents so I gave my phone number to the local health-visiting team and asked them to pass it on to anyone who needed it – any knackered parents who were struggling but had no idea where to start. Within the space of a few months, word had spread about the lady who came into your house and taught your kid to sleep in a few nights, and the phone began to ring. As time went on, I left family after family waving goodbye on their doorstep, their faces brightened by a few short days of sleep. As demand for sleep support grew beyond my capability, I called on my little sister, Gem, to help 'for a bit'. Gem was a practising paediatric nurse at the time and had no intention of ever doing anything other than nursing but she agreed to help until it got less busy. It never did. Little did she know that her offer to help would lead her to her life's true course as she joined her big sister on a solid sleep mission.

Today

Twelve years on, we are immensely proud of our eight-strong team of women, including three NHS paediatric nurses, a senior clinical psychologist and an integrative therapist. We are best known for our life-transforming sleep turnarounds and our compassionate, responsive approach. We are all about being led by your child and not the clock. We don't subscribe to the notion that sleep must be tightly scheduled for it to be sound. Sleep can take any shape at all, so long as it happens! We are often described as the happy middle ground, free of restrictive routines, but with plans that generate highly successful, long-lasting results. Our life's work is not to free families from exhaustion, but to give them the tools to do it themselves. We help you to look at sleep through a holistic lens, listening to and holding space for each family's sleep story and the complete journey that's led them to us. To unlock unbroken sleep, we must first understand the emotional and psychological barriers to it. These are always unique to each family. Once a thorough assessment has been made by our paediatric nurses, we recommend a plan if (and only if) we believe it has the potential to totally turn sleep around. We will talk to a family about whether they need just a plan, or some 1:1 support and handholding too. We've found a clear parallel between the way we guide parents and the way we ask them to guide their children. Our way is inherently nurturing, intuitive and responsive. After all, sleep teaching takes a leap of faith both on our part and the parents'. As we put our complete trust in a parent's ability to do it themselves, we ask them to do the same for their children. It has been a genuine honour to witness over five thousand families across the globe tap into the healing power of sleep and the life that it brings. Seeing parents raise their children with a new-found patience, sense of calm, connection and peace is without doubt the greatest honour of all.

Inaction to Action

The advice surrounding sleep in the early years is contradictory and confusing, leaving many parents stuck in no man's land. This is a bleak and barren place; one of inaction and stagnancy. When we don't know which way to go, we stand still. And who wants to live their life doing that? The words within our book will help you to break away from inaction, moving forward without hesitation. They will allow you to dive deep beneath the surface of infant sleep, revealing the treasure of your intuition. It will help you to discover what's really behind the poor sleep you've been battling so that you can move forward in your own way and on your own terms. No longer do you have to wander weakly through the mist of a shattered life. You and your child are worthy of a daily chance to restore, recoup, repair and recover. This book will act as your torchlight as you navigate yourself away from the dark days of exhaustion towards the bright light of a rested family life.

Who We Are

It might be a good time for us to tell you a little bit about us, your faithful companions on your quest for better nights and happier days. We were born Eve Marie and Gemma Katharine Phillips in 1981 and 1982. We grew up in a seaside town in south Devon with our mum, Pauline, our dad, David, our younger sister, Beth, our brother,

Dom, and our goat, Mandy! It was a happy childhood, filled with warm cornflakes (thanks to Mandy's udder-to-table offerings) and tadpole farming from the river at the bottom of the garden. It was handwritten tickets to family shows in front of the mantelpiece in the sitting room. It was a childhood filled with sky-high pushes on our tree swing; our little legs stretched out and our squinting faces tilted up to the sun, hair billowing, wild and free. It was little feet clip-clopping our mum's high heels down the cracked concrete garden path to fetch the eggs from the chickens. It was our secret language haigy-paigy and Tuesday toffee apples at the Victorian evening in the town precinct. It was hours and hours of dance classes. It was love.

It is only now, as we look back as adults, that we realise how lucky we were. Every child on Earth deserves to feel unconditionally loved for who they are; to have at least one person who believes in them and their ability, without limit. Our parents did just that. We were blessed to be raised by parents who had an abundance of belief in us and our capabilities. We were taught that nothing was off limits if we were willing to try hard to achieve it. The way that we were raised shaped not only how we went on to mother our own eight children, but it became the life source of everything we do at Calm & Bright.

Eve's story

Like billions of parents before me, the birth of my first child had me stumbling along the unforgiving path of sleep deprivation. I obediently accepted the universal belief that the first few years of parenting were supposed to be rough – that sacrificing sleep was totally normal until at least age three. I believed (and still believe) that my main purpose as a mother was to raise emotionally secure, compassionate beings. As far as I could tell, the only way to do this was to meet my baby's every waking need, whether those needs fell in the night or the day. If my baby needed me (or often, in my case, my breasts!) I would come to the rescue. While it was torturous surviving on dregs of broken sleep, it was far more appealing than an emotionally scarred child, which is what I'd come to believe

I'd get if I dared to sleep train her. So, for ten torturous months, I breastfed my firstborn every one to two hours, night and day. The cavalry (breasts) were summoned if my daughter was sad, tired, bored, in pain, hot, cold, afraid, frustrated or in need of a nap. Oh, and when she was hungry! Over the next six years, I was blessed to go on to have three more babies (and a lot less sleep). In the summer of 2015, I had a newborn baby, an eighteen-month-old toddler, a four-year-old and a six-year-old in my care. It was as brutal as it sounds. With broken sleep relentlessly coming at me night after night for weeks on end, and all four children at home because of the school 'holidays', it felt like I was in a wild and wilful sea with huge waves crashing down and knocking me over. Every time I got up, before I could catch my breath, another wave knocked me back down again. I was drowning. One day, I sent a desperate message to my closest friends. It said, 'PLEASE HELP' and then: 'I'm not ok. I need to say it out loud. I don't know how to do it??!! Would anybody come and take the baby to let me sleep for just two hours, please? I am worried about myself.' My friends rallied round. One brought a home-cooked meal. One encouraged me to feed the baby and then took him away until the next feed. Another swept the floor and put a load of laundry on. One took the big kids to the park for a few hours. I finally slept. When I woke I felt uplifted, clearer and hopeful. I hadn't been swept away on a white horse, but I had definitely been rescued that afternoon.

The snippet of sleep got me back on track, but it wasn't long before another wave of exhaustion came crashing down. The broken nights were relentless and unforgiving, showing no mercy, even when I said out loud that I couldn't take it any more. Just when I thought sleep couldn't get any worse, along came another night from hell. Sometimes, it would feel as if the children were tag teaming me. Or as if the universe had something against me. I wondered what I had done to deserve this. On the nights when more than one of them was awake, the time it took to go back and forth between them meant I was surviving on under two hours of broken sleep a night. Even when the children slept, I often couldn't. Falling asleep was never a problem, but any night wake made me so anxious and wound up that I struggled to get back off to sleep, my heightened heartbeat so often pounding in my pressure-cooker head.

Too little sleep across too long a time turned me into a shadow of myself. I'm naturally vibrant, energetic and optimistic, but life was slowly being sucked out of me. To an untrained eye, I didn't look too different (save for the dark circles and haunted eyes). I was very good at saying how 'fine' everything was. Interestingly, our psychotherapist auntie, Beni, jokes that 'fine' stands for:

Fucked-up
Insecure
Neurotic
Emotional

which was more like it! My eyes were red raw, pleading and vacant. I wept, often. Sometimes for no apparent reason. My back pain started that year (from all the hours spent bent over a child in a cot) and this pain continued for many years. Emotionally, I was a frantic pendulum: weepy, snappy, volatile and either completely detached or totally in my feelings. At times, I felt so full of rage that I frightened even myself. I did not know then what I know now: that postpartum rage can present itself in the early years alongside – or independent to – postnatal depression. Parents who experience postpartum rage might find themselves screaming, swearing, lashing out, throwing or breaking things, experiencing violent urges or thoughts or feeling flooded by unpredictable emotions. Such outbursts are often followed by deep-seated shame and guilt. I experienced postpartum rage throughout the early years of my children's lives. I often found myself saying and doing beastly things, unable to access the self-control to stop it. I could hear the awful things leaving my mouth but felt powerless to stop them until afterwards, when my family would cautiously emerge from the wreckage of my words, tentatively waving their white flags.

I shouted or screamed more often than I care to admit. I once broke a light switch by throwing a wicker chair at the wall in anger. Sometimes, as I erupted, which often happened without warning, I found my words punctuated with language that would have made me wince just a few rested months earlier. I knew I was blessed to have four beautiful children, but the exhaustion made it feel more like a curse than a blessing. The guilt that accompanied my resentment weighed heavily on my chest like a thick tar. What more did I want? Why wasn't I more grateful? Why didn't I feel happy? Why did others find it so much easier than me? WHAT WAS WRONG WITH ME?

In the dark and hopeless pit of sleep deprivation, I willed myself to have an accident and be hurt just enough that I could sleep in hospital for a day or two. I longed to trip down the last few stairs as a token accident, but I couldn't bring myself to do it. This wasn't because I was afraid of the pain – physical pain was far more appealing than the tormented state I was in. I couldn't do it because it meant being away from the ones who were the cause of my exhaustion. The ones that I loved the most.

I remember brushing my six-year-old daughter's hair once and even though I knew I was doing it too roughly, in that moment, I didn't care. Another time, when my son got out of bed for the sixty-seventh time in a row (yes, I was counting) I put him back in a little too firmly and held him down on the bed just a little too long. I berated myself the rest of the night. In the early hours of the next day I sat on the floor next to his bed as the birds began to sing, tears dropping onto his hand as he peacefully slept. I felt like the most undeserving mother in the world. There were other times when the exhaustion put me and my family in danger. I forgot the paddling pool was running as my toddler played in the garden. I fell asleep with candles burning. Left the woodburner door open with a frilly cushion just a foot away and went to bed. Forgot to lock the car with my handbag on the passenger seat. Left the front door wide open (we lived on a main road). Forgot to put the hand brake on. Reversed into countless cars/posts/gates/bins. My car was always scratched. The worst, though, was when my second-born was two weeks old and asleep in his car seat in the back of the car. As I drove past a lovely looking pre-school, I decided on the spur of the moment to stop and look around to see if they had any space for our eighteen-month-old. As the manager showed me around, she said, 'Is it just the one child that you have?' To my utter horror I realised that I had left my two-week-old baby in an unlocked car in the middle of February. Without saying a word, I ran out the building and onto the road where I'd parked only to find him peacefully asleep just as I'd left him, but the thought of what could have been still fills me with dread. Every time some sleep-related thing happened, I felt like a hopeless, worthless failure. A really rotten mother.

My exhaustion didn't just impact me. It infiltrated the well-being of my whole family and the close circle of those most important to me. I forgot dates and people who mattered. I sent my son into school in uniform on a mufti day. I forgot about an assembly that same son had a main part in. He had a stammer, and it was a big deal for him to speak up. I forgot about it entirely, but however hard I tried, I couldn't forget his face when he asked me where I was at the end of the day.

It was moments like these that made me wonder if I should really be responsible for my four beautiful children. I was certain they deserved a better mother. On my most exhausted days, I believed they would be much better off without me. With a better person at the helm of our family's ship. I was sure I was a burden on them. Every single time I felt such deep shame, there was a common denominator. The exhaustion. It had seeped into every fibre and function, eroding my rationale and reason. I knew it was the lack of sleep that warped my thinking and prevented me from accessing rational thoughts. But I wasn't able to find a way out.

Today, now that the fog has lifted, I do not blame myself for the times I acted the way I did. I now know that all I needed back then, to enable me to be the mother I was beneath the exhaustion, was sleep. I am able to wrap the old, knackered me in so much love and compassion. I offer her forgiveness rather than judgement for the many mistakes she made. Exhaustion is a brazen thief that robs us of all the good stuff. It steals away with our hope, our rationale, our strength and our resolve. It has the power to trick perfectly decent mothers into believing they are monsters. But it lies. We are immeasurably capable and worthy. We have just been too tired for too long.

Do you remember the car crash that was the beginning of Calm & Bright? That pivotal moment came when I was driving back from a local baby group just a couple of miles away from home. As usual I was doing my best to concentrate on the road with such precious cargo inside, but I was operating on my usual four or so broken hours of sleep and was running on empty. At a roundabout, I checked left and right before pulling out. My tired brain assured me that the road was empty but I had clearly missed another car because before I knew it, all I could hear was a car alarm, a barking dog and my baby's cries. We had both escaped physically unscathed, but I could not shake off the realisation that my baby and I were no longer safe and I could no longer operate on such life-threatening levels of sleep. Before I'd even got back in the car, I knew I had no choice but to sort my daughter's sleep.

Before the crash, I'd been accepting of the broken sleep, believing that there was no realistic alternative. The countless baby books, online forums, unwelcome opinions and guilt-inducing 'experts' made me feel ill informed and overwhelmed, and I did nothing. Phrases such as 'they're only little once', 'they won't need you for ever' and 'babies don't only need you in the day' guilt-tripped me into feeding my ten-month-old baby more regularly than she'd fed at birth even though my gut (and her beautifully chubby thighs) told me she didn't need it. The sleep deprivation felt *so wrong*, yet I turned away from that inner knowing time and time again, trusting instead the incessant external voices that told me that it was *right* to carry on. So, I did. Unquestioning and obedient. *This is what good mothers do*, I told myself. *It's not biologically normal for a baby to sleep through the night. It is my job to protect her from any distress or struggle. It's not supposed to be easy.* I struggled on.

But the crash had presented the undeniable truth. It grabbed me by the shoulders and shook me into action. No longer could I continue, blindly accepting the half-life I was living. I knew my baby deserved more and a tiny voice inside me dared to whisper that I did, too. Despite what I'd been led to believe, I knew deep down that it wasn't supposed to be this way. The very reasoning that had prevented me from acting – that they're only little once – became the catalyst for change. The sentiment that the years were fleeting made me determined that I would be present for them. I did not want to look back, a mother with school-age children, wishing I'd felt more connected to my little ones in the early years. I vowed that I would no longer drag myself through these supposed golden years, longing for the relentless days to end, only to dread the night ahead. In the days after the crash, I said goodbye to the helpless bystander I had become in my own life story. It was time for me to step up; to be the person I needed. So I set to work crafting my own way. Little did I know that this way, which was first scribbled on the back of a torn envelope, would breathe the life back into not only my family, but others.

I had to create my own approach because I was deeply uncomfortable with traditional sleep training methods which seemed to me to be heartless, detached and adult-centred. My mind had been flooded with the idea that sleep training was cruel and damaging, so I wanted to create my own love-led way, which put my baby's emotional well-being at the forefront of anything I did. I vowed I'd always respond to Tilly's needs, saying through my actions: 'My darling, I love you and I will *always* come back, but I am not going to do what we did before because it's not working for any of us.'

I wanted my baby to know that I believed in her and her ability to sleep the sleep she was perfectly capable of taking. I knew that at ten months old she was physically and emotionally able to sleep twelve solid hours a night and I was determined to enable her with the tools she needed to do it. Instead of feeling bad about her needing to be so attached to me in the night, I shifted my thinking to view the bond I had created favourably. Everything that I had done to ensure that she was well-attached in the first half-year of her life meant that the perfect foundations had been carefully laid down for a happy and secure baby. One who had been loved so beautifully that she could access it any time, whether I was right beside her or not. The truth is that she was capable of sleeping well all along, I just needed my belief in her to catch up with her ability.

A week after my decision to take positive action, our mum came to stay for a few nights to support me while I did the sleep teaching. I was terrified and totally dreading it, but my responsive and loving approach allowed me to easily differentiate between my baby's wants and needs. I was finally able to act with confidence and clarity, which was a total game-changer. On night one she did her first ever six-hour stint of sleep. Just three nights later she was sleeping twelve solid hours a night. She was happier, more energised, more interested in solids, more placid and more content. In her awake time she was easier to read. She woke from sleep cooing instead of crying and she seemed to radiate a sense of calm now that her true needs were being understood and met. Tilly is now thirteen years old as I write these words. She's had less than ten broken nights since that day. Part of the reason why sleep training had seemed so abhorrent to me was the notion that she might grow up unattached and disconnected. That she would, as the anti-controlled-crying folk warned, be unable to form healthy relationships or develop a strong sense of worth. If only I'd known then how my baby girl would blossom and thrive when she was getting the sleep she needed and how proper rest would play an immeasurable role in her confidence, sense of self, how she built friendships and how she felt about herself. The first ever baby to be sleep taught the Calm & Bright way has grown up to be a young woman who's the epitome of kindness and empathy. She has an unwavering sense of self and a strong sense of purpose which even some adults would aspire to. She is a beautiful empath with the most wicked sense of humour. She stands at the front of a long line of C&B babes who are living proof of how enabling and life-giving sleep teaching really is.

Gem's story

When I fell pregnant with my first-born, Toby, I had a preconceived notion that when I became a mother, not much would change! I thought I'd take it all in my stride, naively thinking that the night shifts and eight years of paediatric nursing would make my experience of motherhood a walk in the park. Toby was a good sleeper from birth, and I don't mind admitting that I felt quite smug. I thought the reason he slept so well and was so content was down to me! I thought I had it nailed and was the most natural mother in the world. I genuinely wondered what all the fuss was about when exhausted friends of mine were complaining. Then, I had Louis!

I vividly remember calling the hospital when Louis was four weeks old after pacing the house for two hours as he screamed the house down. I demanded to speak to a doctor, adamant that I knew what I was talking about because I was a paediatric nurse. There was something wrong with my baby and they needed to tell me what it was!

As the long weeks unravelled (and after I'd spent hundreds of pounds on cranial osteopathy and rescue remedy!) Louis was diagnosed with silent reflux and finally everything made sense. Why he screamed for the first three months of his life, why he pulled away from my breast constantly, making me feel like a complete failure. Why nothing would sate him. Why it felt like I just couldn't meet his needs. Looking back, it feels such a contradiction that the period that was supposed to be the happiest time of my life was plagued with the darkest times. I remember thinking 'How can I possibly be this tired? Is this normal?' It felt torturous. My ability to function properly and stay connected to the people I loved was deeply impaired. I had an overwhelming feeling that I didn't have the capacity to be who I wanted to be as a mother, a wife and a nurse. There were times when on a nightshift I had to triple check my drugs dose with another nurse, because I knew my brain wasn't performing optimally. This made me on edge all the time and I became a highly anxious person. Once I understood Louis' reflux and how best to help him with it (which I talk about later on) I was ready to tackle sleep in time for my return to work when Louis was six months old. Within two weeks of adopting the C&B approach, Louis was sleeping like a champ and I joined the rested parents club. It turned out to be the best membership I'd ever had.

The Birth of Calm & Bright

Remember how we told you about how Gem came on board at Calm & Bright somewhat reluctantly? While she'd always respected the work Eve was doing, she'd trained hard since graduating from the Florence Nightingale School of Nursing and Midwifery and was fulfilling her childhood dream to save lives. After some *Eve persuading* (this is very different from normal persuading, you see) and some serious deliberation from the queen of procrastination, Gem agreed to help Eve. Five days into her first support, Gem was on the phone to Eve with wet eyes – she realised that she was still saving lives, just in a different way. She was hooked.

From then on in, the team grew. We are now widely regarded as one of the UK's leading voices in paediatric sleep. At the time of writing, we hold the highest level OCN Childhood Sleep Practitioner qualification, which is the most comprehensive training available in the UK. This extensive certification has a focus on a strong and healthy parent–child attachment, which ties in beautifully with our love-led ethos. In addition to this and our twelve years' experience, our team has over forty collective years of paediatric nursing experience. Not only does this mean we can support families of children with complex health needs, it means we're pretty unshakeable. It takes a lot to flap a paediatric nurse because they're highly trained in real-life emergencies. This gives them an enviably calm composure when the heat is on and allows for a huge capacity for care and nurturing.

Our methods and philosophies are based around the very roots of that nurturing and care; of healthy separation, emotional security and a thriving parent–child attachment. Our approach allows children to spread their wings and fly, albeit next to us and alongside us. If we liken what we do to swimming lessons, we do not swim with our babies on our backs. That would be swimming *for* them, which would not save them if they got into any kind of trouble in the water. Instead, we teach our children to swim *themselves*, giving them the skills they need to feel safe and secure in the water. Giving your child the gift of sleep doesn't only benefit them, it brings immeasurable benefits for the whole family. Parents are not only rested but empowered, having made the changes needed for a better life themselves. When we are parenting rested, we are so much more able to serve our little people and ourselves. By keeping our cups full we can pour generously from them when others need us. And let's face it, as a parent, that's pretty much every flipping second of the day!

We once came across a beautiful illustration of a tree with a bird in it. The words read: 'There are two things we must give our children: roots and wings.' Most of us want to provide our children with firm, unwavering roots. Equally as important is granting them permission to 'go it alone'. One of Eve's favourite bedtime stories is *Mole and the Baby Bird*. It's about a little mole who finds a baby bird who has fallen out of its nest. Mole keeps the bird because he loves it. But the wild bird is unhappy and lonely in mole's dark underground room. After some reflection, Mole decides to release his bird, and when he sees him flying free, he is glad. We find it so beautiful that Mole kept his bird close because he loved it. And he let him go because he loved it. This is a beautiful metaphor for the work we do. We hold our babies close and let them free for the same reason. Love.

But it can feel as if sleep teaching is the opposite of loving when you hear statements like 'If you don't see to their needs, they'll stop needing you' are veiled threats re-packaged as golden nuggets of advice. The message is that if you make yourself unavailable to your child overnight, they will not want or need you any more. An unneeded mother! What a way to guilt-trip a parent into staying stagnant in an intolerable situation. The origin of statements like this stems from an innate fear within today's parenting culture of exposing a child to upset or discomfort. Society has swung from raising children at an emotional distance to protecting them from experiencing any discomfort or difficulty at all costs. But the pendulum has swung too far. Never allowing our children to experience difficult feelings gives them unrealistic expectations of life and undermines their ability to form a skillset to cope when they are presented with struggle. Boundaries that are set in place with love are instrumental in a child's confidence in their ability to sort out the things that life throws at them. Our children will push our boundaries and test them in order to be sure that they are safe within them. They will always test us as much as they need to until they are sure and secure. It is our job as their parents to let them know that the limits are there for their benefit and that as adults it is we who make the decisions as protectors of their growing hearts and minds. It is precisely *because* these years are so golden and so fleeting, *because* they are only young once, that we must be as at peace and as present as we can be for the children we have the honour to raise. Having a well-rested family means we can enjoy these precious years to the best of our ability. Being rested expands our capacity to love, nurture and guide.

Twelve years ago, Eve made it her mission to find a love-led way through the sleepless nights and dark days. To become the person she needed. Today, together with Gem and senior sleep supporter Lucy's medical knowledge – and the team's extensive experience – we are here to be those people for you. We are here to enable you with the all the tools you need to figure sleep out yourself. You don't have to choose between a well-rested and a well-attached child. You do not have to drag yourself through these early years or settle for less sleep than your family needs to thrive. You deserve to have the knowledge and the evidence to make up your own mind about sleep, free from anyone else's judgement or shame.

We are here to let you know that you can enable solid sleep just as well as we can. In fact, you can do an even better job, because you have the closest link to the world's best expert on your child; the person who inherently knows what they want and need. The one who has studied your child intently for all their life – yes, you! We will tell you what we know about solid sleep and its barriers, but we will not strictly stipulate what you should do and when you should do it. That is up to you. We have full faith in you making that empowered decision yourself.

By the end of this book, you will feel much more capable of cutting through the confusion and scaremongering surrounding child sleep and you will have a good knowledge of your child's true sleep needs at every age and stage between birth and six. You will feel more in tune with your child, your partner, any other children you have and, most crucially, with yourself. You will learn to trust your judgement again with a new clarity of mind. You will be able to spend your time and energy on the things and people you love. Proper sleep has enabled parents in our care to run marathons, return to work, have another baby, set up their own business or start a project they've always dreamed of. Sleep heals. It just needs to be given the chance to do so. Later in the book we will hear what a leading neuroscientist, mental health psychologist, a doctor and a headteacher have to say about sleep and its impact on family life. We will show you the evidence behind sleep teaching and the origins of the anti-controlled-crying movement, dispelling a great many myths in one fell swoop. We will show how sleep teaching is in perfect alignment with raising an emotionally intelligent, well-attached child. We will share some of the real-life stories of parents we've helped like Sarah, mum to eight-month-old William, who told us on our first phone call that she'd thought about jumping down the stairs because she was too tired to walk up them ever again. And Sally, who was passionately against any kind of crying but spent most of her time doing precisely that before she found our plans.

You do not need the 15,000+ studies into the critical importance of sleep to help you understand how much you need it. You can *feel* it, just as our children can. Any parent who wishes to meet their child's fundamental needs cannot do so without including sleep at the top of the list. It is high time that sleep is viewed as a fundamental pillar of health that we cannot remain propped up without. We need to think about sleep in a new way, addressing our and our children's true needs and giving sleep the importance it deserves.

We will show you the surprising role that you play in your child's sleep and how you hold the key to unlocking a rested life. We will simplify the steps to creating a no-frills sleep environment and we will give you the tools to craft a flexible daily routine that is realistic, flexible and freeing. How can any routine work that insists that a nap must happen at a certain time? What about the other kids? The school run? That lifeline class that you really want to do? How can a nap possibly be at the same time for a baby who wakes at 6 a.m. or 8 a.m.? Surely it's more about the time awake, the quality of sleep up to that point and (most importantly) the baby themselves? What if your child needs less or more sleep than the recommended amount? Where does that leave you and how do you know how to adapt things? We've used our approach to help us navigate a busy family life with multiple children of different ages and needs, and a working life. We've got great pleasure from watching it work for countless other families too. We will give you an unshakeable inner confidence to throw out the archaic sleep rule book and tune in to what you innately already know. We have included some audio resources to support you as you find your way forward, free from whatever has been holding you back. Once solid sleep is in place, we will equip you with the tools you need to future-proof it so that the sleep you enabled stays firmly put. This book will help you step into your power, leaving the helpless and hopeless days of old behind. It's going to put the most precious commodity of time back in your hands. Dare we say it, it will change your life. Are you ready?

CHAPTER ONE

LOVE TO SLEEP

Love

Let's start with love. Because, from the beginning to the end of our lives, love is what we are here to give and to receive. We are going to show you, in no uncertain terms, that you really can love your child to sleep, without guilt or shame. For each parent, how they'll do this will look very different. For some, it will mean giving a great deal of physical and emotional input to their child: the parent playing a central role in their little one's sleep. For others, it will mean empowering their child with the skills and confidence to sleep soundly themselves. Both ways are expressions of a parent's love for their child. Both are the *right* way, because the right way is the one that works for you.

Guilt

Before we begin to help you think about whether sleep is a problem, we'd like to start by clearing the way for such important thinking. We ask you to take a moment to expel any guilt or shame you may have been feeling around sleep. We want you to hear us when we tell you that it's ok. All of it. Your fears, your scary feelings, your hopes and your worst bits (you know, those parts you're ashamed of). Those parts are all essential pieces of the rich tapestry of you. A seed needs to begin in total darkness in order to grow. The stars can only be seen when it's dark. Your worst parts, your intrusive thoughts, your darkest dreams and your deepest fears about your worth are all welcome here, because they're part of you. We hold space for you here, within these pages.

Parenting is super-charged with emotion and hotly debated conversation. And sleep is at the top of that list (along with the breast vs bottle debate – plenty of worms in that can!). We all want to get it right because we love our children, of course, but also because of what our parenting says about us and our worth. The conflict and confusion arise because there is not a definitive answer to what *right* is. This is mainly because there is no one right way at all, which means that most parents are searching for something that doesn't exist. The moment we can accept that there is no one right way when it comes to parenting and sleep in the early years, the sooner we can focus on what feels right for us.

Blame

Too often, parents blame themselves for their child's sleep problems. And it's no wonder. With each month that passes beyond the half-a-year-of-life stage, parents are increasingly subjected to comments and questions like 'Are they a good baby? Do they sleep at night?' Parents are also warned of certain behaviours 'making a rod for their own back' or 'spoiling' a child. These warnings are usually accompanied with an unhelpful prophecy that your child will never sleep alone/outside your arms/in their own bed unless you do something about it. Can you sense our eyes rolling?! This guilt-tripping has to stop. Nothing is for ever. Your worth cannot be measured by how well your baby happens to sleep. Sleep is an ever-changing and transient thing which can be a total head-doer-inner until you understand how simple it really is. Furthermore, children can't be spoiled. How could they be? Babies who have their needs met on demand in the early weeks and months of life are the very babies who are emotionally secure enough to learn how to self-soothe whenever you're ready for them to (note: they're always ready to get more sleep!). Any habits that are relied upon can be gently undone if they stop working and if the time feels right. But they don't *have* to be. You can do whatever you want to do for as long as you want to do it. You can never give too much love, affection, connection and empathy to a child. (Or an adult, for that matter.) We are all wired for connection.

We find it tragic that some parents believe it is possible to respond to their child too much. We'll never forget the day we were contacted by a mum to a three-week-old baby who told us that her son 'wouldn't be put down'. The mum was concerned she would create bad habits if she always attended to him. This broke our hearts! After a healthy dose of listening and empathy, we told this terrified and confused new mum to pick up her baby and love and hold him as much as he (and she) needed for as long as it took. We told her that it is a parent's utmost duty to respond lovingly to their child. We told her that the early months are not the time to be encouraging separation or independence. That her arms were an extension of her womb. That there was nothing to fear in holding him near.

Doubt

Passing comments that instil doubt in new parents often cut deep and stick around. It's not just comments from family and friends that can make us question everything. It might be a strongly voiced opinion in an online chat room. An article in a publication. A tweet or a post on social media. A song lyric. A caption someone shares, or even a slogan on a t-shirt. In today's society it's not hard for doubt to find its way in through the cracks of our self doubt. Add tiredness to the mix and the cracks widen, leaving us vulnerable to attack. There are such wide-ranging sources of information and opinion in today's world and more often than not, it is questionable in both authenticity and reliability. A tired parent can't possibly be responsible for figuring out how safe, effective and evidence-based the information they're digesting is. Doubt is amplified by tiredness. A mind plagued by both stays stuck. And so the cycle continues.

Vulnerability

Thanks to the sudden and often brutal baptism of fire into parenting, vulnerability can quickly join doubt in the mind mix. Any vulnerability we feel about the way we've chosen to feed, sleep, wean or toilet train our baby can come to the surface when a differing view is encountered. It's as if once we've chosen our lane, we feel most confident when we stay in it, with others moving along in the same direction. The more we're exposed to people in our lane, the more affirmed in our opinions and choices we become. When others from different lanes cross our path it can easily knock our confidence and make us question our choices and motivations. But what if there was a way to confidently jam in your own vibrations at the same time as others feeling free to jam in theirs? What if the sound of their music didn't drown out yours? What if their music didn't offend or bother you (nor make you doubt your own choice of music) because you were happy enough not to care? We think it's high time parents are free to make their decisions from a place of inner strength and wisdom, so confident that no one else's path threatened their own. We are here to help you do just that.

We want you to have the courage to do sleep your way, free of shame and guilt. It's about having enough confidence that you refuse to let anyone, or anything, make you feel like you're doing a bad job. Once you have all the information you need to make an informed choice on sleep, it is up to you to walk your chosen path with your head held high. How you do sleep isn't anyone else's business. If you encounter any criticism or cynicism about your parenting choices, know that it will be less about you and much more to do with their own doubt. Because when someone is happy on their right path, they don't have time to look left and right. They're too busy looking right ahead.

Our mission

We have always been love-led. From our first five years, which Eve spent voluntarily helping knackered parents, to our quietly gifted cases that we offer unexpecting families throughout the year, it gives us such a buzz to enable and empower exhausted parents. It's our life's work. We do it to be the people we needed back when we didn't know where to turn. The people we never had. The listening ears, the empathetic voice. The open arms and the offering of total validation and acknowledgement. Nothing more than what every parent deserves.

But it's not just about being supportive. It's also about telling parents the truth. We can no longer watch exhausted mums and dads drip-fed damning untruths and wildly false accusations about sleep teaching. For too long, tired parents have had to absorb information which scaremongers and guilt-trips them into staying stuck. They have had to run the gauntlet of veiled threats about how their child will turn out if they dare to get some proper rest. Enough is enough! Parents deserve to know what we wish we'd known back then: that the peer-reviewed evidence, extensive research and millions of real-life stories out there reflect that solid sleep is abundantly healing. It brings families and relationships back together. It restores our physical and mental health and without it neither we nor our children can flourish or reach our full potential. Not only does our quality of sleep impact everyone's physical and mental health, it's something that is totally within our reach to change. Real, lasting transformations can take place within a matter of days in many cases. Poor sleep is only something you're lumbered with until you decide to change it.

We encourage parents to turn down the noise on the *shoulds* and to drown out the critics. We help families turn up the voice of their instinct and tune into their gut (because the gut *always* knows.) For us, sleep shouldn't be rigid or restrictive. You are running a home, not a barracks, after all. A rested life is not about being a slave to the clock nor getting it right minute by minute, it's about finding a flow that enables you to live your best possible life. We're here to share with you our guidance and expertise and – hopefully – some laughs, a few tears and a whole lot of support and encouragement. You won't find any judgement, shame or guilt here, just a shared vision of better nights and brighter days for you and your family. If you've been looking for someone to have your back, to hear you out or to hold your hand, you need look no further.

What is a sleep problem?

There is no such thing as a sleep problem until it's a problem for you. Take two mothers, each with an eighteen-month-old toddler. Mother one (shall we call her Emma?) is happy to feed her toddler three times a night. She sees it as the only time she gets one-to-one time with him. For her, her toddler is only young once and she loves welcoming his cuddles and kisses at all hours. She doesn't resent a moment of the time it takes to get him to sleep each night nor does she mind the awake periods that occur overnight a few times a week. Emma often sleeps when her toddler sleeps and her body and mind is in good health, as is her toddler too. He's well rested and his appetite isn't impacted by the night feeds. He's happy and carefree and meeting milestones. He's secure and outgoing and developing beautifully. Despite Emma's broken sleep, she feels content, rested and connected to her loved ones. Her partner is supportive of her choices and does not mind sharing the bed with their toddler or sleeping in the spare room. They are a great team. Her other children are well attached to her and enjoy the quality time they spend with her. For Emma, there is no sleep problem and nothing to change. If we could, we'd high five Emma and tell her that she is doing a tremendous job. We'd encourage her to sidestep the neggy Noras, block out the noise, and keep on as she is, with her head held high. We'd tell her not to allow anyone or anything to shake her confidence in the path she's carved out for her family. We'd tell her that she's the expert in her toddler and that anyone who tells her otherwise should do one! Go, Emma!

Now let's meet mother two. Let's call her Harriet. Harriet hasn't slept more than four hours in a row for a year and a half and it wouldn't be an exaggeration to say she feels like she's dying most days. For the first ten months of her baby's life, sleep came in blocks of less than one to two hours. Her toddler's three wakes a night feel torturous and she doesn't know how much longer she can go on. Most days she feels vulnerable and on edge, like she's just not as good at this mothering lark as everyone else seems to be. Harriet doesn't just doubt herself as a mother, she doubts herself as a wife and a friend. She finds simple, everyday decisions overwhelming. She's begun to worry about her and her child's safety when driving because cars appear out of nowhere, even though she's always paying full attention. She'd hate to admit it, but sometimes she despises her partner, even if it's only just for the way she breathes. They fight over who is the most tired and they haven't slept in the same room for a year. Harriet feels disconnected from her partner and alone in it all. She finds herself snapping at her other children, and then feeling desperately guilty about it. She loves her children with every fibre in her being, but daily she feels touched out and longs to hide. She fantasises about running away although she'd never see it through. Harriet wishes most days away, then feels guilty because she knows her children are only young once. She wants to feel present and connected but she doesn't know how. She gets increasingly wound up during the endless hours that it takes her to settle her toddler to sleep at night. She is becoming more and more angry and resentful each time she's woken up. Even at the first sign of a murmur she finds her heart pumping and her jaw tightening. In the unsettled ground of parenting, she can't seem to find her feet for long enough before she stumbles and falls again. She's struggling. Big time. For Harriet, there *is* a sleep problem.

If we were lucky enough to bump into Harriet, we'd give her a mahoosive hug and we'd let her let go first. We'd tell her that sleep can be very different very quickly. We'd tell her there is hope. Harriet would be told not to feel guilty that sleep hasn't yet been solid nor to blame herself for her toddler's sleep. We'd tell her what a great job she'd done up to this point and how proud we were of her for being courageous enough to reach out for help when it stopped working. We'd applaud her for deciding to make the changes her family needed to thrive rather than just survive in this one life. We'd have just as much respect for Harriet as we would for Emma! Go, Harriet!

It would have been easy to add in other factors to Emma and Harriet's stories. We could've included whether the toddlers were breastfed or bottle-fed, whether there were intolerances or allergies to contend with, whether either mother had a career or the opportunity for help such as a nanny or cleaner. Whether they had a chance to rest or how supportive their partners were. But regardless of what variables exist, each family has their own unique set of values, limits and non-negotiables. Parenting decisions such as whether to sleep teach or not must be made using evidence-based information as the driving force, rather than feelings of shame and guilt. From where we are standing, it is just as sad for someone to feel guilty about not sleep teaching as it is for them to feel guilty for doing it. Nobody, including us, has a right to tell you which path you should take. No expert, family member, friend, guru or stranger gets to tell you that there's only one way to get through this. You must be the forger of your own way forward. You don't need to ask anyone for directions. They haven't been where you're going.

The right way

We have yet to meet a parent who doesn't want to be a good one. We make our choices in alignment with what we believe is right. This sounds pretty harmless, but it can prove tricky. The danger of needing our way to be the right way is that it presents a temptation to make others wrong. Psychology has a name for this way of justifying our choices; *avoiding cognitive dissonance*. Parents who choose not to sleep teach their babies may find themselves needing to reject any benefits of it. They may need to tell themselves that sleep training is dangerous, even if their own sleep levels are more so. They may have to believe that the long nights, days and years of broken sleep are worth it. And even more so, that the agony of perpetual exhaustion is crucial to raising a secure and content child. As you can see, the stakes are high, and this is why it matters so much to so many. To avoid having to experience doubt or uncertainty about the way they're raising their tiny humans (which is an experiment no one wants to get wrong), some parents need to remain fiercely entrenched in their chosen view.

While this is a really easy trap to fall into – one we ourselves succumbed to when we were fervently anti sleep teaching – it's a really counter-productive way to operate. In stating that our way is the right way, we make the mistake of thinking that we are everyone, or that everyone is us. Our choices can be the right choices for us, but they can't possibly be the right choices for everyone. How can they be? Our choices are based on our personality, our upbringing, our culture and our own personal constraints in terms of time, money and energy. No person is the same and their choice has everything to do with them and nothing to do with you. Sleep choices have a direct impact on a person's quality of life and only one person is qualified to make those choices. (Spoiler: that person is you.)

Self-belief

By the end of this book, our hope is that you will be fully clued-up on the facts about sleep. But most importantly, we want you to realise that you're the one with the power to set yourself free from the clutches of a sleepless life. We may have the tools to get you out of the cave, but it is you who will carve your own way to freedom. Finding your way to better sleep is a journey of self-discovery. It will require you to dig deep, to separate your needs from your child's and to take a leap of faith. But you don't have to make that leap alone. We are right here with outstretched arms, ready to take your hand to guide you to the other side.

A Psychotherapist on Sleep
Anna Mathur: Psychotherapist, Author and Speaker

I've been the mum who sought guidance to help all three of her children sleep, so that she could sleep too. I've been the one whose child simply couldn't sleep, due to silent reflux. And I've been the mum who couldn't sleep due to a buzzing mind, even when given the chance. I know tiredness; what it does to my sparkle and my mind. I know how exhaustion steals the ease of my laughter, how it sucks the energy I need to rationalise anxious thoughts, navigate a flippant remark from a family member, or coach myself through a wave of scroll-induced comparison. I know how tiredness causes me to react rather than respond intentionally. How it prevents me from being able to act and parent in a way that is in line with my heart.

I remember when I was particularly sleep deprived, questioning my sanity as the tears came without warning. My world seemed dark and heavy as I dragged myself through it. I was awake every 45 minutes reinserting a dummy, desperately trying to return us both to the restful state we needed and yearned for. As we worked on sleep, I remember waking up one morning after four hours of consecutive sleep and feeling like a new woman. After just one night of better sleep, the tears didn't flow quite so readily that day, and my smile felt less forced. I faced the 'shoulds and the shouldn'ts' of people's opinions about sleep teaching but I knew that for us, this gentle guidance was the path to the return of our laughter. And laughter has always been a therapy for me. We both needed gentle guidance in returning to that and it felt like giving ourselves a gift.

Before you find yourself slipping into the habit of thinking that rest is an indulgence, consider this. Rest is a fundamental human need. You do not need to earn it, explain it or justify it. You just need it. Don't underestimate the energy expended in raising a baby, or in processing the life shifts you go through in the early years of parenthood. While some days it may look on paper like you've done little more than feed, change and wash, your mind and body are increasing in capacity at an alarming rate as you find your feet.

Getting the rest you need is about respecting yourself as a human being. Rest allows you and your little one to recover from a busy day or a testing morning. It also allows you to replenish energy stores so that you can deal with the next curveball, nap refusal or unsolicited comment from a well-meaning lady in the supermarket queue. You deserve far more than to live life as a mother from the bottom of a burnt-out barrel. Rest enables you to gather the much-needed energy to rationalise those anxious thoughts, to laugh, to make decisions, to enjoy those good things in your life. So next time you feel the guilt, feel the guilt and rest anyway. You're doing what you need to do, and in time, as you appreciate and honour rest for what it gives you, the guilt will ebb away. For the best thing rest and sleep gives you is the ability to be more you.

CHAPTER TWO

BECOMING A PARENT

Birth

For a few fortunate new parents, the birth experience is an uplifting and self-affirming one that provides a smooth and pleasant transition into parenthood. For many others (us included), the birth of your baby turns out very differently than you'd hoped. If this is closer to your experience, you may have found yourself with a kaleidoscope of thoughts and feelings post-birth, many of them unpleasant and unwelcome. The triumph of birthing your baby into the world is often clouded by an overpowering sense of pain, failure or injustice. Some women feel robbed of their right to have the birth they felt they were entitled to.

The time that follows birth can feel isolating and lonely at the best of times. Many women who have given birth and experienced their maternity leave during the global pandemic of COVID-19 tell us that they have a strong sense of injustice at not having experienced the kind of support that a pre-pandemic world would have offered them. All feelings are valid and must be given a voice. We like to think of feelings as better out than in, so talk about your experiences and feelings whenever possible to help you process what happened and why. It'll help you to forge connection with others via a common ground and shared experience. Part of the support we've been offering to new parents for the last decade includes talking about birth and the feelings attached to it. To be able to hold space for the mothers we support while they talk about their journey to birth and early motherhood. This enables us to understand and connect with the families we support on a deeper level. It is the perfect start to our journey of supporting them with sleep.

We often refer to the fourth trimester period as being almost like an invisible umbilical cord, in terms of attachment. Your baby is outside of your body and no longer physically attached to you by the cord, but through your responses you nurture your attachment in a different way. During the immediate few weeks after birth, do all you can to take the pressure off you and your baby. Imagine that you're floating in the water, submitting to the tide, wherever it takes you. It's a lot less tiring than swimming against the current! Try not to worry about creating 'bad habits', because there is no such thing. Tuning in to your baby's needs gives you permission to just be. Nurturing your babies as they transition through the early weeks means that later on, whenever you're ready, you can start to gently set the scene to help with confident settling. Still responding and still nurturing, just extending that umbilical cord a little more in the ever-evolving dance of motherhood.

Early weeks

We think it's wonderful how mother nature has a patient and gentle way of easing us into life with a new baby when we consider how sleep takes shape. For the first two weeks of life, your baby is likely to be sleeping most of the time while you begin to recover from the emotional and physical wounds of birth. Babies of this age are awake for just a few hours a day (around eight out of twenty-four hours) and this is your chance to take things as slowly as you possibly can. Here are some ideas on how you can use this time to recover from your birth, physically and mentally:

△ Let everything else go to pot

△ Stay in your pyjamas. This sends a clear message to others and yourself that you're not operating at normal speed or capacity

△ Do one thing that deeply relaxes you every single day (Gem's was a lavender bath, Eve's was daily foot rubs!)

△ Eat and drink to nourish and comfort

△ Talk about your experience as much as possible

△ Cry – your tears will be cleansing

Give yourself full permission to concentrate on responding to your baby's needs without any over-thinking. At the very beginning, these needs are often as simple as being held, fed, changed and soothed. At around two weeks, your baby will be a little more awake and alert as they begin to explore their incredible new world. Even then, their needs are simple and predictable: they need to be fed, to feel physically and emotionally secure, and to sleep. During those early weeks, your brand-new human is establishing themselves in the world. Try to let all pre-determined ideas or instructions from the multiple sources in today's world fade into the background as you focus only on two things: what you and your baby need. If your baby doesn't want to be put down in these early weeks, don't put them down. If they cry when you bathe them, hold off on the bathing for now and try again later. Let your baby's reactions guide you in your care of them.

This is not the time to worry about creating bad habits or 'spoiling' them. A baby cannot be spoilt! There is no such thing if your goal is to raise a confident, calm and content child. Parents often get in touch with us in the early weeks worrying that the only place their baby will sleep is on them or with the help of motion. This is completely normal and to be expected in these early days. The most important thing at this stage is that you and your baby take the time to recover, heal and rest. It matters not how this takes shape so be open to contact napping, naps in the sling, naps in the pram with motion and safe co-sleeping. Simply do whatever works for you within safe-sleep guidelines. Please refer to the Lullaby Trust for ever-updated advice. We will talk more on safe co-sleeping in Chapter Six. Remember, if it's working for you, it's working.

Matrescence

When a baby is born, so is a mother; each vulnerable in their own way. Like the remarkable human face, every woman's journey to motherhood has echoing similarities, but no two stories are the same. For some, the journey to motherhood begins long before those two blue lines appear. Others might find themselves unexpectedly pregnant, having never planned to get there and with no suitcase packed for the ride! In whatever manner a mother is born, it is important not to forget the enormity of the transition a woman goes through to bring her little ones earth-side and raise them once they're here.

As I – Gem – write this, I am going through my eighth pregnancy (I have miscarried four babies and welcomed three into my arms). So I find it very apt that I'm writing about the transition to motherhood as I live through it myself. The journey Eve and I have been on to become mothers has been a weary and weathered one at times. But mothers we are. And good ones at that. Still learning, still adjusting, still faltering and failing on the daily. But deserving. *Always deserving.*

The journey from woman to mother sparks a great upheaval of everything that was, in order to make way for everything that will be. The offering of your body to enable new life, the often-subconscious grieving of your life as it once was and the new identity you have yet to adopt in the world creates a radical transformation of body and mind. During your adolescent years, when your body morphed and your hormones raged, you most likely felt at times like your body was not your own. Most of us bolshied our way through the teen years as irrational, emotionally volatile and anger-filled teens in foreign bodies. The topic of adolescence has had papers, books, articles and studies written on it. Comedy sketches and plays have covered it (Kevin the teenager, anyone?!). Adolescence is normalised, understood and supported by society. We educate our children at home and in school about it, because to normalise something is to understand it. But up until recently, we haven't had a mainstream word to describe the transition from womanhood to motherhood. The term 'matrescence' has only recently been brought to our consciousness by Dr Alexandra Sacs, a psychiatrist who works with pregnant and postpartum women. In her 2018 Ted Talk she described how she noticed a pattern in her work with women over the course of a decade. New mothers were coming to her saying 'I'm not good at this. I'm not enjoying this. Do I have postnatal depression?' They were expecting to feel whole, completed by their baby, to feel happy and to instinctively know what to do.

Yet Alexandra was hearing from hundreds of women, each of them concerned that something wasn't right. She didn't know how to help these women at first, because telling them they weren't clinically depressed wasn't making them feel any better. She wanted to find a way to normalise and name this universal transition, to explain that there is a fundamental difference between having a disease and feeling discomfort and fear about what's happening to your mind and body during such a life-changing shift. Like adolescence, matrescence is not a disease, but is often confused with the more serious condition postnatal depression (PND).

The conflicting, all-consuming emotions and vast overwhelm we feel in early motherhood are easier to understand when we consider the 'push and pull' concept that Sacs and other maternal psychologists and scholars such as Barbara Katz Rothman, Professor of Sociology at the City University of New York, speak of. The pull is biological, as the bonding chemical oxytocin connects us with our baby on a cellular level. That pull is strong for good reason: human babies are particularly dependent as far as earth species go. Unlike many animals we share the planet with, our babies can't walk or feed themselves. Perhaps evolution recognised this by gifting human mothers with the most impressive hormone of all – oxytocin. This so-called love hormone increases around childbirth, breastfeeding, bonding and during skin-to-skin touch. Oxytocin helps a human mother's brain focus on the baby as the very centre of her new world.

But there's a pull in another direction. Each mother has a world outside of her child; her own interests, beliefs, values and things that she holds dear. This is the emotional tug of war we can now recognise as matrescence. Understanding the natural progression of matrescence can help us acknowledge the significant emotional conflict a mother encounters. Embracing it will help ease the strain, shift the stigma and help countless mothers feel less alone on their journey from women to mothers.

Parenting can be shite

An important part of our mission over the last decade has been to encourage women to step into their own power; to give them permission to talk openly and honestly about the tough, unsteady waters of motherhood. There is way too much shame attached to admitting that this parenting lark is really shitting hard at times! If we're going to change the way our society understands this transition to motherhood, women (and men) need to be talking to each other, not just to us. Each time we talk and share, we can understand one another on a deeper level and better support one another. But this is not solely about nurturing our relationships with ourselves as mothers and with other women by talking more. When we acknowledge, understand, preserve and nurture a separate part of our identity, the one which makes us feel most like ourselves, we also leave room for our children to develop their truest parts of themselves. To lead by example in this way, by designing your days to craft an authentic life that you love, is to be part of a life-shifting movement that has the power to positively impact generations to come.

Gem's story

After the birth of my eldest child, I was hit by what I now know was the great wave of matrescence. I remember feeling as unsteady as I'd ever felt. The exhaustion had well and truly hit me and the realisation that this was my new normal, that this baby was here to stay, was a sharp blow to the system. The permanency. The all-consuming intensity. The *love*. I vividly remember lying in a hot, deep lavender bath a few weeks in and just weeping, occasionally immersing my face under the water to let it absorb my tears. The release, the overwhelm, the angst, the relentless exhaustion. I remember feeling worried that these feelings would never go away. The overriding question that kept coming to my mind was, 'Why do I still feel so low four weeks on?'

Like countless women before me, I wondered if I had postnatal depression. I had an incessant internal dialogue that persistently told me 'You're not cut out for this. You're failing! It's not supposed to feel *this* hard! No one else is struggling like this. Pull yourself together.' The build-up of broken sleep, the hormonal shifts and the pendulum-like spectrum of emotions was too much to bear. I thought my instincts would kick in and that I'd be able to read my baby's cries, but I couldn't. It all just sounded like noise to me. Society's unrealistic expectation of how smooth the transition to motherhood was supposed to be had me feeling like I didn't measure up.

When we change our perception of what a good mother looks like, we free ourselves and the mothers to come. When we support and understand the mother, we tell her that she is not only deserving, but entirely worthy. A good mother is not a perfect one. A good mother does the best she can with the tools she has. A good mother is someone who forgives herself daily and in turn teaches her children to do the same.

Phases

We have eight babies between us, yet each time we enter the next phase with our children it's as if we've forgotten everything! When you reach potty training stage with your fourth child, you might think it helps to have been through it with three children previously, but let us tell you that this is not the case! No matter how many times you've done it, with each new baby you become a new mum again. It's as if your brain has to forget all the info from the last stage so you can clear space for the next. Be prepared that each time you face a phase with each child, it will be different in some way. Acceptance of this, and the offering of grace to yourself, makes it much easier for you to be as forgiving of yourself as you are to others. This starts by tuning in to *your* reality of motherhood and lowering your own expectations about how things are supposed to look and feel.

The fourth trimester

The fourth trimester is the first three months of your baby's life. It's a time of transition for both parent and baby, as you get to know each other, adapt to your new world and build your attachment. At the time of birth, a baby has spent three trimesters – forty weeks or thereabouts – being fed on demand and rocked and soothed to sleep, safely cocooned within you. For us, the fourth trimester is about extending that care. The theory is that human babies are born before they are developmentally ready, because of the large size of the human head. The concept suggests that human babies could really do with another three months in utero with all the peace, warmth and nurture that comes from being cocooned safely away inside the haven of their mother's womb. Human babies rely on their parents for much longer than any other species, being born solely reliant on us for survival. When we consider this concept of total reliance, it helps us to surrender to those first twelve or so weeks, to let go of how we think things should *look*, and instead connect with how they *are*. If we spend the first three months trying (and invariably failing) to fit our new, ever-changing human into the boxes we or society prescribes them, we set ourselves up for continual disappointment and feelings of failure. You'll find some guidance on helpful responses and approaches in our obstacles section of the book a bit later on.

Four-month sleep regression

The four-month sleep regression has a lot to answer for. The very mention of it can incite terror in even the most relaxed of parents. It's hands down the topic we get asked about the most. This is because it can wreak havoc in the most settled of sleepers and it's shrouded in mystery with there still being so much that the scientific world has yet to discover about sleep. What we do know is that the four-month sleep regression coincides with a physiological shift. After the first three months, a baby's sleep begins to consolidate as their brains shift from an infant sleep brain to an adult sleep brain. This process of forming and linking different areas of the nervous system happens at the rate of knots and causes varying degrees of disruption for each baby.

But it's not all bad. This is the stage when Mother Nature steps in to lend a hand by prompting your baby to produce melatonin to aid their sleep. This is when short naps will no longer serve your baby and they may become more sensitive to becoming overtired (the silver lining being longer naps). Now more than ever, make sure you are aware of the best nap gap for them and their sleep needs. Remember, however rough it is, it will not last for ever. By six months of age, it is perfectly reasonable to expect that the dust will have settled and that those eleven–twelve hour nights of sleep – with a night feed if you wish – are entirely within reach.

Asking for and accepting help

Ask for and accept help as often as you can. Consider it as a challenge. Imagine that every time you ask for or accept help you get a shiny gold star. Try to accrue as many of these as you can. We can most definitely recommend staying in pyjamas for as long as humanly possible after giving birth – we used to aim for two weeks minimum even if we felt good. Doing this gives a clear message to those around you (and to yourself) that you are not yet healed and need to be handled with gentle care.

Eve's story

I remember buzzing with a strong sense of accomplishment and empowerment while whizzing around Tesco on day four of having my fourth child. 'I've totally got this,' I told myself, boasting to anyone who'd listen that the baby strapped to my chest was only FOUR DAYS OLD! I was desperate to prove my capability and worth in the competition of all competitions. But the only one I was competing with was me. It was almost as if there was a medal I was gunning for, as I'd get a score at the end of the shopping trip to measure how well I was doing. The reality was that I got into the car and wept uncontrollably. I'd refused to listen to my body, and it had increased my postnatal bleeding to warn me I was doing too much. It wasn't only the physical implications of 'powering on' that I suffered from that day – I set myself back by a week or two mentally, as well.

There is no medal for being what you think is 'Supermum'. If she did exist, Supermum would make sure she looked after herself too because she's smart. Consider the analogy of the oxygen mask on a plane – we are asked by the cabin crew to put our masks on before we tend to our children, or we risk running out of enough air to be of help to anyone else. Parenthood requires an insane amount of sacrifice and service, but that doesn't have to be at the expense of your own physical and mental health.

It helps if you can prepare yourself (however unnatural it feels) to respond immediately when people offer help with a convincing 'Yes, please!' Follow it up quickly with something like, 'It would be utter heaven if you could have my elder child for a couple of hours/ cook a meal/ throw the hoover over/ give my feet a rub – that would be amazing.' People offer because they mean it. But if you don't take them up on it straight away, the offers soon disappear into thin air. The first few weeks of your baby's life is the time to 'cash in' on such offers. Even if you're having a good day (you know, one of those 'totally nailing it'/ 'I might even have another one' days?!), just take it! Tomorrow may well be a whole new story. On that note, don't be surprised if a 'nailing it' day is followed promptly by a 'I cannot go on for one more minute' kind of day (or five). It took me four children and six years to realise that asking for help was not only an option but an obligation to myself and my children. Ask for and accept help.

Nurture and mother yourself

In the early weeks and months of motherhood it's important to hold space for yourself in a nurturing capacity. This is a time when we are naturally on our knees with exhaustion and sometimes it can feel like a huge strain just to get through the day. In times like these, the 'nurture you' stuff goes to the bottom of the pile, doesn't it? It's almost a bit annoying to hear as it can feel like there's no time to fart, let alone take a hot bath. But this is the very time when you need it most. Your greatest need for self-care is *now*. Just to be clear, this isn't about lavish spas and time away from your baby. Although it can be! It can sometimes just be taking it day by day and going easy on yourself. It's about using simple skills like mindfulness to allow you to find peace by sitting with your emotions, to give them space and validation. It's about reflecting and stepping back. Being more present. Not trying to achieve so much, and reframing achievement to be less about what has been *accomplished* and more about what *is*. Honour yourself and every little win, even if that's just showing up.

Here are a few simple ways to honour yourself:

△ Start or end each day with five conscious breaths

△ Allow yourself to drink a hot drink

△ Pay attention to how you feel, good or bad

△ Hold space for the ugly, unexpected bits

△ Have a good cry

△ Pick up the phone to a close friend or family member and tell them how you *really* are

△ Acknowledge your little wins

△ Remember what you did right today

As you can see, honouring yourself does not have to be about grand gestures. If you can hold space for yourself for a few minutes a day you'll be more aware when you are not feeling quite right. And when you can be aware of it, you can do something about it. When it gets overwhelmingly tough, try to sit with it. Try to remember that tomorrow will surely come, and it is a whole new chance to start afresh. A crisp new clean sheet.

Your inner critic shouts rather than whispers when you're a new parent so it's important to counter that with sure and steady self-praise. If you find self-praise hard, perhaps seek out someone you can trust who always makes you feel better about yourself and let them remind you of how wonderfully you're doing. Try not to feel any pressure to become the parent you're not. You may not be whizzing up organic purées a month in advance and your kitchen floor might look more like a cow shed, but you may have the loveliest voice that your baby's brain is thriving on. Or you might make a mean bacon and egg sarnie to nourish yourself with. It's about tapping into what your strengths are and what feels good and right for you, and doing everything at your own pace. Slow and steady wins the race.

Talk to your partner if you have one. Sometimes they are the single other person in the world who has an insight into how you're feeling and where you're coming from. Even if they feel like the last person you want to confide in, try to let them in. Let them help you and hold you – even if they're not doing it quite right (they probably won't be, but they certainly won't if you don't tell them what you need and how you need it). Communicate. Remember this is a huge transformation for them too. Help them to help you.

Gem's story

When I had my first child, I barely noticed that James was struggling to adjust too. It's normal for us to lose our capacity to consider our partner's perspective when it's taking all of our energy just to get through the day. But we learnt that talking and giving each other space to feel how we felt helped us feel more of a team. When you know better, you do better (my favourite Maya Angelou quote). Lean on one another if you can. It'll help you stand up taller.

Sleep is not a test

We want to take this opportunity to set the record straight about 'good' and 'bad' sleepers because there is no such thing. Sleep is not a test to pass. It is not something you can fail at either. Your worth as a mother or father cannot and must not be measured by how well your baby happens to sleep. Sometimes nature dictates that your child will struggle to sleep as easily as the next child (highly annoying) but this is not only ok, but entirely normal. Few sleep journeys are without obstacles. After all, we are raising precious children, not robots or soldiers to obediently stand in line or fit into prescribed boxes.

It is perfectly ok to have challenges and setbacks, and this is not your or your child's fault. Valuing and aiming for the best possible sleep must be balanced out with the acceptance that sleep is not always a linear journey. Sleep very rarely comes without setbacks, even for us professional sleep practitioners! Parenting can feel like one step forward and two back at times, and sleep is no exception. The great news is that there is *always* something that can be done to make sleep better than it is. There is always light and always hope, even in the direst of situations. To get help you have to ask for it, and only you can do that.

Riding the waves

Life with a baby is not meant to be perfect. As well as being deeply affirming, love-filled, blissful and rewarding, it is messy, unpredictable, ugly, testing, exhausting, maddening, boring and lonely. Something that's really helped us both is to consider motherhood as a tide, with often conflicting currents. A rip tide, if you like. When we are out of our depth in the sea, we are advised to surrender, to lie back and float to safety. This is because when we try to swim against a tide, we wear ourselves out (and can ultimately drown). When we tilt our head up to the sky, raise our limbs to the surface, take the pressure off and just *breathe*, we allow ourselves to float where the tide takes us. This helps us to gain the strength to swim back to firm ground and a safe shore when the time comes.

The same is true for the first few months of motherhood. It needn't be a battle to get your baby into a routine or sleeping through the night. Parents who can confidently accept that this thing called parenthood is not a race acquire total freedom to do their baby's life at their own pace. You might find yourself being dragged into the funnel of child comparison thanks to stories of Karen's wonder baby who took her first steps at six months, or Alice's son who was born reciting Othello's soliloquy backwards. If you do, try to amuse yourself by imagining our babies all grown up on their first date. They're hardly going to be asked when they first pooed on a potty or slept through the night, are they? Try to cast all unnecessary pressure aside and go with wherever you're taken, through the tough days and the good days and everything in between. To help you ride the waves, some parents find having a routine comforting and reassuring, while others find it a stifling recipe for failure. Whether you're more of a go-with-the-flow parent like Eve, or you feel happier with a bit more structure to your days like Gem, our advice can be adapted to suit you and your life.

CHAPTER THREE

WHAT IS NORMAL?

In this chapter we are going to explore what is considered normal in relation to baby and infant sleep. We'll share with you our experience of working with thousands of families over the years and our personal experience with our own children. We'll draw on Gem's knowledge as a children's nurse of twenty years and the many books, articles and studies we've analysed from experts all over the world. We'll talk about the difference between what is biologically normal and what society tells us is normal. If you're interested in delving further into the data, studies and peer-reviewed evidence, we have popped our favourite sources and further reading at the back of the book. We know that some parents find comfort and clarity from reading the science first-hand, and that others would rather stay up *all* night with an overtired baby than wade through small dense text about sleep! The choice is yours.

Let us begin by talking about normal. Normal is defined in the *Oxford English Dictionary* as 'conforming to a standard; usual, typical or expected'. We don't know if you have *met* a baby yet, but the ones we've encountered have *nothing* standard, usual, typical or expected about them!! There is no profession, book or class that can prepare you for every parenting eventuality or tell you exactly what's going to happen and when. While that might sound somewhat terrifying, it can also be incredibly freeing to accept that *nobody knows what they're doing* most of the time. Most of us are just winging it and hoping no one notices. We've told you our secret now, don't judge us, ok?!

While there is no neat box labelled NORMAL that fits all the infants of the world neatly inside, there are patterns and behaviours that help us understand what is reasonable to expect at each age and stage. What we know to be true from our experience over the last decade supporting families from Hargate to Hawaii, is that true freedom and peace (and a much happier existence) often comes from a parent's ability to release the worry about what's normal, using it as a point of reference only, in favour of tuning in to your child and what feels good and right to you.

The first three months

Imagine for a moment that you are called for an audition. The brief is that you're in one of the happiest times in your life. You're asked to act as if you're filled with elation, wonder, complete love and in a surreal haze of total bliss. At the same time the director wants you to portray all-encompassing overwhelm and despair. You need to show a deep sense of a loss of identity and of confidence in yourself. You're asked to feel these feelings all at the same time. The spotlight comes on and it's over to you. This is an impossible ask, right? Yet this is exactly how a woman feels in the time after becoming a new mother. All at once a giddy kaleidoscope of new thoughts and feelings envelopes our every day. It is brutal, beautiful, bewildering and blissful. In the first three months it is completely normal for your baby to wake and need you frequently through the night. To be held close, changed, fed or winded. It's usual for babies of this age to need a lot of help and support with sleep. There is nothing more natural than your baby wanting to be close to you during this time. Babies have an innate need for parental sensory stimulation like smell, touch, sound and motion. Like all primates, babies have a biological need to be in close contact with their parents. This closeness and nurture might mean endless contact napping, baby wearing, safe co-sleeping and hours of settling and soothing on demand. Your baby might experience a day/night reversal of sleep due to sleep patterns that are a bit all over the place.[1] This is all biologically normal.

It's not until your baby turns three months that they will start producing the hormone melatonin, which gently and naturally creates a more regular sleep rhythm. It's also super normal for babies of this age to grimace, suck, mildly jerk about or seem restless. This is how normal active sleep looks and does not mean that your baby's sleep is disturbed.

At this age, naps can last anything from ten minutes to three hours and stints of sleep between one to four hours are typical overnight. You do not have to worry about getting your baby into a routine or aiming for them to sleep through the night at this stage, although you can if you'd like to. While some babies will naturally take longer stints of sleep from very early on, sleep is extremely changeable at this time, and it's usual for there to be no apparent rhyme or reason. Taking the pressure off you and your baby during this period of heightened uncertainty will make for a much less fraught experience for both mother and baby.

We know that in the early months babies are not programmed to sleep through the night. Irregular sleep patterns and frequent wakes for feeds are what is biologically normal. What society per-ceives as normal in these early months can be hugely conflicting and is often based around whatever 'flavour of the month' is in the media at the time. Depending on when a tired parent hits the search bar, she may either believe that she needs to co-sleep with her baby or put them down to sleep. That, coupled with the well-meaning advice from a friend or family member (cue mother-in-law saying 'Oh no, mine never did that,' me: You have a short memory; or 'Be careful not to build a rod for your own back', me: If you're not careful, I'll stick that rod where the sun don't shine!!), it's no wonder new parents are left feeling confused about what normal 'should' look like!

Let us put your hearts and minds at ease. We say this to you as mothers, as friends, as sleep supporters and as nurses. The only predictable thing about the first few months of a baby's life is how unpredictable they are. We've consciously avoided telling you too much about what they're capable of sleepwise because it's so varied and changeable. We hope this helps you to reduce any pressure or expectation, allowing you to be present in – and maybe even enjoy – the marvels of new life.

Four to six months

It's at this age when we probably see the most push and pull in relation to what is biologically normal and what society perceives as normal. At a time when parents are only just emerging from the first three months, they are met with an avalanche of conflicting opinions and societal *shoulds*. Parents who reach out to us at this time often tell us that they feel as unsteady on their feet as they did in the early months. They feel almost in limbo – stuck between life with a newborn and a baby who is halfway through their first year. Parents tell us they feel unsure how to move forward, knowing that by six months most babies are able to sleep through the night but not knowing how on earth to get there. The good news is that by five to six months healthy babies are capable of sleeping eleven to twelve hours overnight with a night feed if desired. They also start being able to knit their sleep cycles together in the day, with naps lasting between forty-five minutes to two hours.

The Sleep Foundation describe this three to six months stage as being a time of 'major changes and development, activity and sleep'.

This leads us on to talk in more detail about one of the most widely searched topics – the four-month sleep regression. There is a reason why this particular topic is such a huge talking point. As we mentioned earlier, the four-month sleep regression can cause complete and utter havoc.

Luckily the four-month sleep regression is so called for a reason. The disturbance need not last longer than the five-month mark and there is so much that you can do to support the best possible sleep before that.

At this age, naps typically last between twenty minutes and three hours and stints of sleep tend to range from three to eight hours. This is a good time to start thinking about how you might like sleep to look in the second half of your baby's first year. You might find it helpful to think about the following questions to help you reflect:

△ How happy are you with how sleep is now? Stop here if you're delighted!

△ Are you feeding your baby at the same frequency as when they were newborn?

△ Do you feel that every feed is necessary?

△ Is how you put your baby to sleep working for you, your body and any other children or family members?

△ Is your baby getting the rest they need?

△ Are they waking happy?

△ Are they happy between sleeps?

△ How good and right does sleep feel to you?

If you find yourself happy with how things are when reflecting on the questions above, do not change a thing! The entire premise of our work is about finding what works for you and doing just that.

Gem's story

I remember as a first-time mum being terrified of 'that regression' everyone warns you about. I think I must have spent several hours googling it and having my worries validated by every mum's forum going. Hell, this sounded rough! And this was all before Toby had even reached four months. No matter how hard I searched I couldn't find a positive outcome or story. Had I known then what I know now, I would have given myself a massive hug and said that this regression is tough but fleeting and that brighter days were literally just round the corner.

In a time of such big change, we recommend keeping your responses small and simple. This means tuning into your baby's own needs and not taking drastic measures. It means keeping an eye on nap gaps to avoid overtiredness, gently reducing night feeds when you feel ready, releasing the pressure to compare your baby to others and gently laying down the foundations for self-settling by giving them the occasional opportunity to have a go at getting themselves off to sleep.

It is around this age where you might start venturing out to baby classes and meeting other new mums, which invariably means sharing your experiences of motherhood, including those wonderful birth horror stories. Chatting about your experiences and how your baby is getting on often coincides with that dreaded comparison creeping in. It might be that before this you felt pretty damn good about where you were. It can take just one comment from another mum about how they're loving it, how their baby is sleeping through already and how they're thinking about having another. Cue you instantly feeling like the shittest mother in the world. Shall I let you in to a little secret? They're lying. Ok, so that might be a *little* extreme, but even if they are telling the truth, motherhood isn't linear and you don't know that things won't take a turn for the worse the very next day. Or that some areas of motherhood that you find simple are a real struggle for them. Remember not everyone wears their struggles for all to see, so try to take their views or accomplishments with a pinch of salt.

I remember feeling sure that every single mum at my baby yoga group had it nailed. And they didn't just *look* like they had it all together, they waxed lyrical about it. The funny (or sad) thing is that despite feeling the opposite, I told everyone how well I was doing too! I remember driving away from that baby group each week feeling utterly crap. I felt like I was the only one whose baby wasn't sleeping and I didn't measure up. So I ended up spending the whole class under a complete façade, lying that sleep was great when it was total toss! It wasn't until years later when the mums in the group had become firm friends (you know, the ones you can be brutally honest with?) that we all admitted to one another that we lied our way through baby yoga. None of us had our shit together and we were all putting on this massive act because every one of us all felt like we were the only ones not coping. This is precisely where societal expectation comes in. We all believed our babies should be sleeping through the night when in fact not one was. We had each been subjected to repeated subliminal messages that our bad days needed to be hidden. That a good mother always gets it right.

Eve said it well when she wrote her poem 'Bad Day':

You are not your bad day,
Nor the mistakes you make,
You are not the words you shout,
Nor the meals you make.

You are not the tears you cry,
Or the time it takes,
You are not the things you forget,
Or the cakes you don't bake.

You are not the sleepless nights,
Nor the broken days,
You are not the endless struggle,
Nor the foggy state of daze.

You are not the things you tell yourself,
You're not what they say you can't do,
Don't fool yourself that you're not enough,
We both know it's not true.

You are brave.
You are light.
You are strong.
You are might.
You are courage.
You are dear.
You are loved.
Have no fear!

Six to twelve months

Let's start by talking about what babies of six to twelve months are capable of in relation to norms. Healthy babies and children have the physiological ability to sleep eleven to twelve hours overnight, taking lovely long naps in the day lasting up to three hours. It is during this time that babies will transition to two naps, which happens at around six to eight months. Society tells us that broken sleep is normal until twelve months, but the reality is that our babies are capable of solid sleep long before then.

We define *solid* sleep as a length of sleep either in the day or night that a baby or child takes themselves without needing parental input. It's important to mention here that this does not mean that they don't come into light sleep or stir in that time. Human sleep cycles happen in five stages, four of them N-REM sleep (non-REM). It is entirely biologically normal (and essential) for our little ones to cycle through light and deep sleep. Evolution made it so, so that we could spot the bear in the cave or the snake on the rock. It is what happens when they fall asleep or wake from that sleep that determines whether they need us or not. If every time they wake, we feed, pat, rock or re-plug the dummy, they come to rely on this input to continue sleeping. This doesn't mean they *need* a dummy put back or a feed to sleep, rather that they have become used to getting one. This is the time when gently creating space between anything your baby relies upon to get to sleep and sleep itself can be a good idea.

It's important to consider that separation anxiety can occur around this time (typically between eight and eighteen months). It is normal for obstacles such as teething, wind, poo, and developmental changes such as crawling and standing, to disturb your little one's sleep momentarily. Gem talks at length about health obstacles in Chapter Eight.

There continues to be a significant amount of confusion in relation to what babies are biologically capable of in this age bracket and what society deems as normal. This undoubtedly adds to the anxiety surrounding sleep, and leaves parents feeling like they're in limbo. The parents we support tell us that this time is very much a phase of 'wait and see'. Waiting for sleep to improve, waiting for their babies to start doing longer stretches or dropping night feeds themselves. Not acting because sleep is bound to improve when their babies are ready.

But what if we told you that it's less about *them* being ready and more about *you* being ready? That parents in their hundreds wait for several months for sleep to sort itself out, when in fact it could have been remedied within a week. While there's nothing wrong with waiting months or years for sleep to improve, you don't *have* to. There is so much that can be done to transform sleep with the right tools and expectations.

Twelve to eighteen months

Mothers with children of this age are often the most reluctant to reach out for help. They tell us that this is due to a fear of judgement because they're still feeding their baby to sleep. If this is you, that inner voice might be saying 'It is time to make some changes now', but your heart might be pulling you in another direction. As your baby's first birthday approaches it can be a time of reflection and mixed emotions. Those last firsts often make us want to press the pause button. Be gentle with yourself as you transition on to the next chapter and feel all the feels. The best is yet to come.

Sleep really can be steady and solid in the main part. The main challenges are the two to one nap transition (which happens at fifteen to eighteen months but can begin as early as ten months) and the often emotive start to nursery, which can bring the delights of coughs, colds and bugs along with it. This age is when your toddler may need to learn to take their sleep out and about, either due to them being cared for in another setting or because of commitments out of the home. This can breed anxiety for parents who have sleep sorted or who never have. This is when it's best to let your child sleep when they're tired, try not to allow a bad nap to make a bad day and to always fall back on an early bedtime when your child needs it.

Naps will typically last between one and a half hours and three hours, with eleven to twelve hours overnight. There is not a nutritional need for a toddler of this age to have any milk overnight, either breast or bottle. That's not to say you can't give milk or cuddles if you want to, so long as you do not mind the disturbance it will cause to your and your toddler's sleep. Separation anxiety can raise its head at any point in this age bracket, but this needn't pose much of a disturbance to sleep. In fact, a rested child is so much more emotionally resilient that you will find them far better equipped to handle any big feelings they encounter.

These early toddler years are a time of transition both physically and emotionally and sleep is the glue that brings it all together. During this time, sleep really can be steady and restorative. These toddler months are fleeting and if you're able to reap the rewards of solid sleep it makes for a much happier existence for the whole family.

Eighteen months to three years

As your toddler grows and develops, discovering more about the exciting world around them, there can be emotional changes that take place. This is a time when your child starts getting a real sense of self in relation to their place in the world, outside of the safety net of you. They are building their trust and extending their emotional bonds, they might even be forming young friendships with their peers at nursery or preschool. As your child grows and begins to assert their independence it's normal for them to start to test the boundaries. This can feel like a challenging time (it's not called the terrific twos after all) and while Eve and I have felt like pulling our hair out on many an occasion, we do believe that much of the difficulty at this age can be traced back to insufficient sleep.

While sleep doesn't change much in this age bracket (toddlers still need a nap lasting between one and three hours, and eleven to twelve hours overnight) it is important for parents to know that this is a typical age for boundary testing to take place. We are often approached by parents whose toddlers have dropped the nap at age two but, despite refusing the nap, are absolutely shattered and are falling asleep in their spaghetti bolognese. This is almost always about the toddler exerting their will and autonomy so convincingly that the parent finds themselves swept along by it despite their child's glaringly obvious exhaustion. In this case we'd always advise a return to the nap even if that means a snuggle on the sofa or forty winks while out and about.

Try not to compare your child and their friends when it comes to dropping the nap. If your child is the only one who needs a snooze while his friends continue to play, so be it. That is what is best for him and that is what you will do. You'll be the smug one who gets to take a breather anyway – make the most of it!

Most toddlers transition from a cot to a big bed by the end of their third year, but please do not rush this. Here are our reasons why: if it ain't broke, don't fix it. If they still physically fit in it, are not climbing out and are sleeping well, ask yourself why you want to change it?

It's much easier to implement loving boundaries when your baby is still in their cot. Your child will have a better understanding of the cot to bed transition the older they are.

At this age, your child only tests for as long as they need to until they feel safe in your responses. As soon as they feel that your responses are consistent and safe, they will stop testing. Alongside being firm with your boundaries, you can practise connection over correction. Here are six of our favourite ways to connect with your child:

△ Talk quietly and slowly

△ Five minutes of complete attention can turn the whole day around

△ Eye-level listening

△ Hide little love notes in their lunch box

△ Tell them three things you love about them

△ Let them end the hug

Three to six years old

The start to pre-school and reception often follows six weeks of later nights, potential holidays or weekends away and, if we're lucky, later mornings. In our houses, summer holidays usually look like under-the-stars sleeping, firefly walks, endless summer nights at the beach, camping in the garden and mandatory 'midnight' feast – never later than 10 p.m. In short, sleep generally being less structured and consistent. This coupled with the emotional and practical upheaval of a school start can result in highly charged emotions and frazzled or anxious parents. This can have a significant impact on boundary testing, and bedtime is a classic time for this to arise. We can't tell you how normal this is; if your child is to feel confident enough to navigate life without you for those six hours a day, she needs to have a strong sense of her own autonomy and capability. Let her act it out, safe within your loving boundaries. That's not to say that you have to accept bedtime battles without any hope for change. Understanding why struggles have arisen doesn't mean you need to stand by helpless. Action can be taken with the right information and support.

When Gem and Lucy were practising school nurses, they discovered a running theme with children who were struggling at school. They found that it wasn't out of the ordinary for older children to be experiencing sleep issues and that if sleep wasn't sorted by the time a child started pre-school or school, it had a huge impact on the whole family. Many of the mothers they encountered were feeling too ashamed to ask for help and some had even told their Health Visitor that their issues had been resolved, for fear of judgement. Many of their referrals came from teachers who identified exhaustion as a factor in a child's struggle in the classroom when it came to concentration, emotional resilience, the ability to form friendships, tolerance of difficulty and learning capacity.

Let's talk now about another normal occurrence in children of this age. Dreams and nightmares often occur in children aged between three and six due to their rapidly developing brains, newly found curiosity and changing thought processes. While dreams and nightmares are extremely common and need not be a cause for concern, they can cause short-term disruption with sleep and children wanting to seek additional parental reassurance. If your child is experiencing frequent recurring dreams or nightmares, we recommend helping them process their thoughts and feelings in waking hours, meeting emotional needs and reassuring them as needed. Dreams and nightmares are vastly different from night terrors, which happen in only 3–6 per cent of children. For information on this much less common challenge, please refer to Chapter Eleven.

In the introduction, we talked about our two hypothetical mothers, Emma and Harriet, to show that a sleep problem is only a sleep problem if it's a problem for you. But many parents need something a little more concrete than that. They want a reference point to begin to think about whether and when they might wish to seek help with sleep.

The Australian Research Alliance for Children and Youth (ARACY) paper 'Understanding and Responding to Unsettled Infant Behaviour' is a great point of reference for parents who think they may have a sleep problem. It defines infant sleep difficulties into two simple categories:

1. Difficulties getting to sleep – persistent crying when put to bed or being dependent on suckling, rocking, being driven in the car or other associations to go to sleep

2. Difficulties with sleep maintenance – short daytime sleeps, frequent overnight waking and resistance to re-settling if awake after a short sleep.

This definition covers a broad spectrum of sleep struggles, which include, but aren't limited to:

△ Night waking (that is not caused by hunger, pain, discomfort, or disturbance) beyond the age of six months

△ Multiple feedings in excess of nutritional requirements

△ Bedtime battles

△ Periods of awake time overnight

△ Naps which take an age to settle them for, only for them to wake too soon from them

△ Exhaustion disguised as separation anxiety (preventing parents from making changes for fear of the situation worsening)

△ Early wakes before six a.m.

△ Night terrors

△ Sleep transitions including naps, moving out of the parents' room, moving into a cot or bed

The ARACY paper outlined several ways in which sleep issues impact a family:

△ Great demand on parents' capacity for emotional self-regulation and empathy

△ Diminished parental confidence and feelings of helplessness

△ Poorer mother–infant relationships

△ Poorer maternal mental and physical health

△ Severe maternal exhaustion

△ Feelings of depression, frustration, anger

△ Marital dissatisfaction and tension

△ Poorer quality infant care-giving

These points are completely in line with what our C&B families have told us over the last twelve years. Luckily for us, and for you, some of them have allowed us to share their stories with you. We've dotted them throughout the book in the places we think you'll find them most helpful. Names have been changed where requested.

All of the points above are valid reasons to seek help with sleep, yet some parents feel they have no choice but to accept broken sleep beyond the point of their baby's biological capability (and their own tolerance.) This might be down to their social demographic; perhaps they have only one child, or do not have to return to work, or have support in place to enable them to live alongside broken sleep longer than other parents. For others, their decision might be impacted by other children that need to be considered or a job to return to. Some will prioritise sleep for the benefit of their mental or physical health. Some will have no choice but to get sleep on track. Whatever your reasons for working on sleep or leaving it as it is, remember that breaking away from what seems to be the norm is not only ok but sometimes the best thing you can do for your family. We wonder how many positive changes came about in the world because of someone refusing to accept a norm that didn't align with how they wanted to live their life. Regardless of whether something is labelled as normal or not, if it doesn't *feel* right, it probably isn't.

To relate this to sleep, just because eight out of the ten babies in your mother and baby class are still waking overnight doesn't mean yours has to. Just because they *don't* sleep doesn't mean they *can't*.

Accepting a societal norm can not only result in months or years of unnecessary broken sleep, it can also be dangerous. How many mothers who needed professional treatment for postnatal depression never sought it because they were told what they were feeling was normal? How many mothers have put their baby's screaming down to a developmental leap when they needed medical attention? If you have any concerns that something isn't quite right, we urge you to seek additional support from your local healthcare practitioner. Make your own informed decision about whether you want to work on your child's sleep, based less on what is *normal* and more on what feels right and good in your gut.

In this chapter, we've explored what's considered normal for each age and stage of sleep in your child's life. We've drawn on our knowledge as paediatric sleep consultants, as nurses and mothers and our extensive experience and research in our field to give you this information. We've shown you what healthy babies are biologically capable of and we've spoken about the push and pull between what is *possible* and what society tells us is *normal*.

For every parent, the knowledge of what's normal needs to be balanced with what feels right and sustainable. The threshold for when to make changes to sleep will be different for every parent. The threshold is different for everyone, and no one can judge you for where yours lies. We love *The Completion Coach*, Wendy O'Beirne's analogy of this. She says you wouldn't walk down the street, knock on your neighbour's front door and ask them to decorate it to your liking. It's their house. And their choice. Their threshold. When it comes to your parenting choices, it's your life and your decision. When you find yourself seeking validation from external sources, try to tune in to what's within. Why spend time foraging the wild and unpredictable forests for firewood when your own garden has all you need to stay warm?

CHAPTER FOUR

THE GREAT DEBATE

Eve's story

Twelve years ago, when I was a first-time mum, it seemed to me that parents had a choice of two extreme camps when deciding on their approach to sleep. Camp one seemed to think sleep training was the stuff of the devil, its very notion barbaric. On the modern battlegrounds of social media forums and chat rooms, this camp hissed vitriol at any parent who dared to make sleep better for their family, warning them that their selfish choice would result in their child feeling abandoned and leaving them psychologically damaged. Camp two appeared to be all for it, shutting the door until morning, obsessively following their military precision routine no matter what. Their children slept, sure, but at what cost? Both sounded pretty godawful to me, so I steered clear of both camps, wishing there was a happy middle ground that I could reside happily in, with children who were well attached *and* well rested.

Little did I know that I'd go on to build that place from the ground up myself, welcoming all the other parents who didn't identify with either extreme view. Back when I was a new first-time mum, the camp one posse saw sleep training as brutal, neglectful, out of line with biological norms and – often the favourite – *a load of bullshit pseudoscience*. They argued that sleep-taught babies would feel so neglected that they would struggle to form healthy attachments to you and anyone else in the future. The people from this camp weren't shy in their opinions, I soon discovered. They freely unleashed a torrent of wrath against anyone who dared to suggest that there might be an alternative to dragging your exhausted arse up to the sacrificial mother-altar to surrender your very sense of self in exchange for the emotional security of your child. Like all good mothers, I wanted my child to be emotionally secure; but I didn't want it to be true that I had to lose myself in the process. The way I saw it, the more *me* I was, the more *them* they could be. There was no question that the sleep deprivation was making me a lot less me – at times, I didn't recognise the person looking back in the mirror.

During my time at camp one, I learnt with horror how sleep training was just the birth-child of a modern world, how the relatively new concept had been created with the goal of making babies fit neatly into their parents' schedules, causing the least inconvenience possible. It was inherently selfish. Parents shouldn't have children if they didn't want to be inconvenienced, I learnt. I read shocking stories of children only stopping crying because they'd given up hope that their parents would ever come. I was told that even if they did finally settle peacefully in their cots without tears, that the cortisol would still be pumping fiercely through their veins. It seemed that my baby's peaceful slumber came at too high a cost; that of their little brain and body being stressed out (at best) and long-term damaged at worst. Sleep training was a poison that I'd give my child in return for a rested life. A poisoned chalice. Like millions of mothers before me, I decided not to drink from said chalice. I was out. I surrendered myself to last place on the pecking order of needs to be met and staggered on, broken and bruised, resolute that I'd done the honourable thing and picked my baby over myself. Like a good mother should.

I soon learnt that camp one spent a lot of their time fuelled by outrage and wired by exhaustion. At first, I quite admired their passion; it was deeply persuasive and kind of exciting. It swept me along as if I were a part of some movement. Like I *belonged*. This sense of belonging came during a period of motherhood-imposed identity loss. I remember being asked by someone at a party once what I liked to do for fun and feeling very upset that I didn't know the answer. I could have spent all day reeling off my children's likes and dislikes. I realised then that I could identify more closely with my children than myself. What *did* I like to do? Who *was* the person my children called Mum? I didn't know because I was never able to look her in the eye for long enough to find out. In finding my feet as a mother, I had lost my grip on myself.

The offer of community and common ground felt almost im-possible to resist. When I was out and about with other mums (which didn't happen too often as I was usually too shattered to do much more than plonk unsuspecting child in front of CBeebies) I quite enjoyed reeling off the occasional 'fact' about sleep training and how awful it was. My favourite snippet to share was how a sleep-trained baby's brain was pumped *full of cortisol*. I mean, I'd read it on social media, so it must be right, right?! Sharing what I'd learnt helped me to feel informed and (if I'm honest) powerful in a time of total powerlessness. Clinging on for dear life to the so-called facts helped me to justify why I did nothing about my own child's broken sleep which, if I was honest, was breaking me into tiny shards day by day. I had to vilify the other side to justify my own.

But the more time I spent at the anti-controlled-crying camp, the more a sense of unease began to creep in. The cracks began to show, at first as tiny fissures and then as a gaping crevice between what they said and what I felt. The more I read and heard from them, the more keenly I had to scour their words for the gentle, nurturing and compassionate approach they told us we should always offer our babies. Through their confrontational, accusatory words and wolf-pack mentality, the gentle camp was anything but gentle. Like vultures, they would swoop down on their unsuspecting prey (usually some vulnerable and shattered mum on a forum or page desperate to get some sleep) and the dressing down that followed was uncomfortable to watch. Gradually I began to spend less time on their pages, choosing instead to occupy no man's land where I wasn't against sleep teaching nor passionately for it. I decided, after the best part of a year, that these were not my people after all.

I now know with the benefit of hindsight that these mums weren't all bad at all – far from it – they were just like me. They too had been fed the untruths about sleep teaching and they recited them blindly like a creed. Under their armour of exhaustion was a mum just like you and me, desperately trying to do the right thing for their child, and needing to be sure that they were doing it right. Like mine, their view of their worth as mothers was tainted and twisted by sleep deprivation. Beneath the tip of the iceberg of anger was the pain of a life without sleep. And the doubt that they were on the right path. We were all looking to find our camp. Our identity as mothers. Our village. If only we had known this, we could have focused on what united us rather than what drove us apart.

After I left camp one, I didn't spend any time in camp two as I had already been brainwashed by my many months of living in the other camp. In my propaganda-filled, sleep-deprived mind, I figured I already knew a heck of a lot about camp two. From what I'd been told, these guys had no problem shutting the door to their child's bedroom at night, having whipped them off the breast as soon as possible, if they breastfed at all. Apparently, they looked scathingly upon mothers like me who chose to co-sleep, breastfeed on demand and who put their baby's attachment above all else. I felt as if these kinds of mums would roll their eyes whenever I complained of being tired. I once heard a mum at the park saying that she was convinced that some mums just wanted to be martyrs. That they had nothing else to talk about other than how tired they were, despite knowing that they could sort it out within a few nights! Good sleep was a choice, she said, and they were making the wrong one. Mums like these appeared to me to be abandoning their children until morning, once their child had obediently taken a full night's sleep. I definitely didn't belong to that camp either. To my dismay, neither perceived belief system sat comfortably with me, so I continued to wander aimlessly about the deep and dark forest of opinions, warnings and waggling fingers. And never-ending, relentless *guilt*.

The agonising decision

Thanks to the camps of opinion I have just written about, I was totally torn on the topic of sleep teaching. I would even go as far as to say I was in agony over it. I've outlined my fears for you below in the hope that if they resonate with you they may be able to help you to unlock your own. Who knows, perhaps some of our fears will be the same, even a decade after I felt mine. You see, the sleep debate is an eternal one. The same fears that gripped me back in 2009 are the ones parents come to me with over a decade later. Here are just some of my fears about sleep teaching from all those years ago.

Me then: my child will only need me for a short period of time. I should make the most of it while I can, as these moments will not last for ever.
Me now: these years are indeed fleeting and short-lived. This is precisely why I need to be rested enough to enjoy and be present for them and breathe them in without resentment.

Me then: I've read sleep training damages the parent–child bond. I will not sign up for something that threatens that in a gazillion years. (I liked to be dramatic back then, too.)
Me now: nothing erodes the parent/child bond more than exhaustion. It is a toxin that infiltrates every aspect of our health and happiness. Our exhaustion-busting work over the last twelve years shows us time and time again that a rested family is a more connected, happier and harmonious one.

Me then: I've been told there is cortisol present in a baby's brain when they are sleep trained.
Me now: the 2012 study that looked at mother–baby cortisol levels showed that babies' and mums' cortisol levels were the same before the training and after they fell asleep following training. The only noted change in cortisol levels was on the third day (when none of the infants cried because that's how quickly sleep teaching works)

due to the mothers' cortisol levels reducing. All this showed was that mothers are more relaxed after the sleep teaching has worked, somewhat unsurprisingly![2]

Every time I had a night from hell (you know the kind, I'm sure) my interest in sleep teaching was piqued. But it never materialised into any action because among the other mummies I hung out with, in the online support groups I visited and the whispers of the playgroups I dutifully dragged myself to, sleep teaching was a dirty word. The dirtiest. And besides, it was *perfectly normal* for your child not to sleep for the first three years of their life, wasn't it? Everywhere I looked, it seemed as if tired parents wore their exhaustion like a badge of honour. How tired we were was our favourite topic in the parks and places we met. It was almost like there was a club, with a rammed membership and a lengthy wait list. Being in the club had some perks; it meant you had a fail-proof topic of conversation with virtually any other parent on the planet. It was used to justify why you weren't able to do x, y and z, and it gave you the perfect excuse to stay in whatever situation you were unhappy with. It brought us all together. But being in this club chipped away at your very soul. It sentenced you to the status of 'passive bystander' in your own life. Exhaustion was a club all right, but it wasn't one I wanted to be part of.

Everyone else seemed to be coping with the exhaustion just fine, so I formed the conclusion, like millions of mothers before me and countless others yet to come, that the problem was not the exhaustion, but *me*. There was no way in hell that I was going to ever leave my baby to cry, as I saw it back then. No matter what it took, no matter how irretrievably I would fall apart, I vowed that I would always see to my baby's needs night and day and that I would not under any circumstances let her struggle. It didn't matter how much I suffered – just that she had everything she needed, with me being top of that list. I just needed to suck it up. Because what kind of mother takes part in something rumoured to be neglectful, harmful and cruel? Who signs up for that? *Bad mothers*, I presumed.

Back then, in my exhausted and vulnerable sleep-deprived state, I was incredibly impressionable when it came to the misinformation about sleep that I was force-fed. I'm going to outline below my staunch beliefs at the time and directly underneath each belief I'll show you what I now know to be true thanks to the benefit of twelve years and extensive training and research in my field (oh, and the immeasurable benefit of a rested mind).

Sleep teaching means ignoring my child's needs.
Sleep teaching the C&B way is highly responsive, intuitive and love-led. It never includes ignoring a child.

People only do it for selfish reasons.
There is nothing selfish about wanting to meet a core human need for your child and you.

Parents who sleep train are trying to make their baby fit conveniently into their life.
Wanting adequate rest for your family is not convenient, it is essential for your family.

You shouldn't have children if you don't want to be woken in the night by them.
Becoming a parent needn't mean total sacrifice of self. A parent running on empty isn't beneficial for anyone.

Sleep teaching will ruin the bond between my child and me.
Long-term exhaustion erodes attachment and threatens family bonds more than a few nights of sleep teaching ever could.

Sleep-taught children grow up to have difficulties forming meaningful relationships.
There is zero evidence to support this and in fact the opposite is true. Sleep teaching the C&B way contributes to peace of mind, health and happiness. Solid sleep is a balm to the human mind and in turn to the relationships we forge.

My child will only stop crying because she will learn that I will not come.
Does a child only learn to ride a bike when they give up on our presence? No. My child stopped crying because I taught her to feel secure and confident enough to do it herself.

My child will feel abandoned and her trust in me abused.
A child's trust in their parent is enhanced when all parties are emotionally present and available. The research is clear: sleep aids in this dramatically.

It's not possible for babies to self-settle.
Every time a baby sleeps longer than a sleep cycle, they are settling/self-soothing. All babies are born with the ability to self-soothe. Evidence suggests it is we the parents who interfere with that natural process.

It is perfectly normal for a child under the age of three to wake multiple times during the night and to need a parent.
It may be something some children do, but this is not necessarily because they need to. It is often because they have not yet learned to self-soothe. Providing they're in full health and are feeding well in the day, babies above six to eight months do not need to wake overnight.

Even if it works it won't last.
We often hear from families several years later who are still enjoying the benefits of a full night's sleep. Our sleep teaching lasts because our plans don't only fix the issue, they provide parents with the tools to future-proof sleep. Many parents on our plans tell us that they used them to help instil great sleep from the start with any subsequent babies!

I am a bad mother if I decide to sleep teach to get sleep for myself.
Sleep gives us access to a whole new toolkit of energy, patience, compassion, nurture, clarity of mind and openness of heart. Deeply beneficial qualities to show to our children and ourselves.

The truth

To understand why sleep teaching has historically had such a bad press, it is important that we understand where the arguments against it originated.

Warning: the following information contains deeply troubling and potentially triggering information concerning the neglect and abuse of children. If you need to skip ahead, please do.

In December of 1989, the abhorrent Romanian dictator Nicolae Ceauşescu fell from power. Among other heinous crimes, he had forced women to have multiple children to fuel the country's economic growth. Invasive investigations of women were carried out to ensure they bore at least five children and those who bore ten or more were rewarded with The Heroic Mother award. Ceauşescu once announced 'The foetus is the property of the entire society' and 'anyone who avoids having children is a deserter who abandons the laws of national continuity.'[3]

As a result of Ceauşescu's ruling, Romania found itself with more than a hundred thousand children living in over six hundred state-run orphanages across the country. As families grew beyond their control, many couldn't afford to feed or care for their children. Thousands of parents abandoned their children every year, swamping state orphanages.

Within these establishments the children lived in despicable conditions. They were starved of food and left in soiled nappies. It was often extremely cold and there were many cases of pneumonia. The children were subjected to beatings, humiliation and sexual and emotional neglect.[4] These children had their most fundamental human needs unmet and abused. Between 1966 and 1989 there were between 15,000 and 20,000 child deaths in Romania's children's homes. It wasn't until 1989 that the Ceauşescu regime was overthrown and aid groups were finally let in to the country.

The Romanian Study

A long-term study of 165 Romanian orphans who were brought to the UK in the early 90s explored the devastating impact on those children in later life.[5] Of those who spent more than six months in the orphanages, four out of five had far higher rates of social, emotional and cognitive problems later in life. Common issues included difficulty engaging with other people, forming meaningful relationships and problems with concentration and attention levels which continued into adulthood. This group was also three to four times more likely to experience emotional problems as adults, with more than 40 per cent having contact with mental health services. Despite their low IQs returning to normal levels over time, they had higher rates of unemployment than other adopted children from the UK.[6]

Comparing the incomparable

You might wish to take a breather for a moment here, before you carry on. We know we do. It's traumatising enough to even con-template this kind of neglect in innocent children, let alone to live it. But it is critical that we apply the necessary perspective here. The inhumane treatment these children endured is barbaric. It cannot be compared to gently teaching a child to sleep over the course of a few nights. Babies and children who are sleep taught are safe, warm, loved, fed, well and inherently secure both in the physical and psychological sense. They are never ignored. Never left for lengthy periods of time to go it alone. They're not left for months without human contact, nor are they subjected to physical or emotional abuse or neglect. During sleep teaching, parents are responding lovingly to their child throughout the very short length of time that it takes to enable them with the life-skill of self-settling. These children are loved beyond measure. They are blessed to spend their days eating fresh food, playing with their siblings, visiting outdoor spaces and watching smiling faces move as they engage in conversation. They sleep in a clean, comfortable and safe place, with toys that they learn from and are stimulated by. They are warm. They are clothed. Their nappies are changed. They have parents who love them so much that they want to enable the best possible sleep for their family. What happened to those poor children in Romania is completely incomparable to a few nights of sleep teaching.

Reframing sleep teaching

Now that we've explored the origins of the most fervent arguments against sleep teaching, shall we take a moment to explore how 'bad' it really is to enable your child with sleep? First, it's important to talk about the difference between cry it out and controlled crying. Cry it out (or CIO) involves putting your baby or child onto their cot or bed and leaving them to it until they fall asleep, without any input from you. Effectively, shutting the door on them and not returning. This is entirely different from responsive controlled crying where a baby is supported and reassured throughout the process. At Calm & Bright, we practise highly responsive, baby-led enabling, which allows parents to forge their own way based on what their baby is telling them. Through our one-to-one support, parents can access compassionate guidance and expertise from one of our sleep supporters. While some parents don't experience any protest, the likelihood is that parents will be faced with a few nights of upset and protest. The tears are not something that sleep teaching brings, nor is it about *leaving* a child to cry. Rather, the tears (if they come) are in response to the changes parents make for the better. Gem has a brilliant saying: 'the level of protest will always be proportionate to how much the change is needed'. In other words, the more dependent the child is on the way they get to sleep, the harder it can be to undo. Even so, almost all cases where the sleep association has been built on over more than a year are still usually resolved within a week or two. Remarkable, really!

It is unlikely but possible that some families will have a real hard slog of a few weeks of sleep teaching, for the most ingrained of cases, or ones where the process is interrupted by teething or illness. But even then, we are not talking about fourteen nights of crying. Nor are we talking about a child being upset half of a night, or a quarter of a night, or even an eighth of a night. We are talking about lovingly attended-to upset that comes in response to the healthy, positive changes you are making for the greater good. What 'attended-to upset' means in reality is being physically and emotionally present to support your child as they learn. It means offering continuous reassurance and comfort each time they need it. Just like teaching your child to ride a bike, it means stepping back a little when they're getting it so they can taste that unbeatable feeling of mastery and accomplishment, but keeping close by to grab that saddle again if they start to wobble. It means saying to them through your actions that you are always there. That they can trust in their needs being met and rest easy in your judgement of what those needs are. It means communicating to them that everything you do comes from a place of love and hope. That you've got this. That you've got them.

Most families experience a breakthrough almost immediately, with countless parents reporting total turnarounds by nights three to five. When there is no upset at all, which happens more regularly than you might think, parents are struck by the realisation that their child wanted (and had been perfectly capable of) sleep all along. It was the parents who needed to catch up with the child, not the other way around. Time and time again, parents say that the only regret they have is that they didn't do it sooner.

Thinking differently about crying

We like to share our seatbelt analogy with parents who struggle with their child being upset. If your two-year-old refused to be plugged in the car and was getting very upset and frustrated about it, you wouldn't say 'Don't worry, darling, we can't bear the thought of you being upset, so go ahead and leave your seatbelt off. We'll drive around at 70 miles an hour and hope for the best – so long as you don't get upset.' Instead, most parents would insist their child kept their seatbelt on for their safety, no matter how much their child raged. As parents it is our duty to give our children what they *need* over what they *want*. That means making important and difficult judgements about what is best for our children until they are old enough to do so themselves.

Parents who decide to sleep teach often tell us that there are far more tears before the sleep teaching than during it, both from the parent and child. It is rarely a happy existence that motivates a family to make changes to their sleep. Families who turn to sleep teaching do so because their current situation isn't working for them, and life is pretty unpleasant. We've been told more times than we can remember that sleep teaching is often far less stressful and tearful than an average bad night. Our C&B families tell us that when sleep teaching is met with tears, they feel at least they are taking positive action for change rather than rocking a distressed and wakeful child who wishes they were asleep as much as the parents!

Don't be afraid of tears

No one wants their child to go through any unnecessary upset. After all, isn't it our job to be their protector, to keep them safe from harm? Mothers have had about 200,000 years of programming to condition them to find out what's wrong with their baby and stop it. A mother's primal instinct is to soothe, comfort and ensure the survival of her baby. So it's understandable if crying stirs up big feelings. These feelings are completely natural. We have yet to find a parent who hasn't worried about how upset their child will get. But a parent who finds protest hard to bear is not weak, or not cut out for sleep teaching, they are simply *a good parent*, one in tune with their baby's true needs. It is this attunement that will lay down the perfect foundation for parents to guide their little ones to the happiest sleep outcome.

It's important not to sugarcoat how the protest or upset can feel. We've yet to find a parent who likes to hear their baby cry (thank goodness!). Most find it difficult to hear and some find it intolerable.

These feelings aren't always just about the crying though. They can sometimes be more about how a parent interprets and internalises those cries. For example, what crying/distress/struggle has meant to them in the past and how it made them feel at the time. Parents who find their child's upset intolerable may wish to view it as a signpost to dig a little deeper before embarking on any sleep teaching. Reading Eve's poem (on page 242) can be useful in helping you to think about separating your needs and your child's.

It is quite a shift to reframe your child's upset and change your usual responses to them, but it's important to remember that nothing changes if nothing changes. During sleep teaching, we are still responding, still nurturing, still meeting needs, just in a different way, one that may work far better for your family. Something feeling *hard* does not mean it's *wrong*. Plenty of *right* and *natural* things are hard. Just take birth. As a parent, it's not our job to avoid our children ever getting upset or struggling. Whether we like it or not, life will present them with a whole host of struggles; a series of hoops they have to jump through; a lot of them when we are not there to lift them through. If we don't let them practise jumping those hoops while we're there, what will they do when we're not? When as parents our minds and bodies are rested enough to spend their childhood equipping them with enough love and adventure and the strongest sense of self, they will tackle any struggles they face with gusto. They can jump those hoops themselves, with us cheering from the sidelines.

Many parents feel liberated when they learn to reframe their child's upset. Tears do not mean that what you are doing is wrong. Tears come for some children on being told they can't have the toy in the shop they had their eye on. But we don't necessarily give them the toy just to avoid upset (although, to be honest, I might if I was really knackered!!)

If as parents we can reframe struggle as a positive thing, as an opportunity for growth and triumph, we can take a lot of the pressure off ourselves and our children. We can step back and let them live with the space and freedom to explore and discover their own unique set of skills and life-tools. If, when your toddler struggles to open a jar, you open it for them and hand it back, then sure, they'll be happy, but they won't have the same look on their face (or feeling in their proud heart) as they would if you secretly loosen it and hand it back, allowing them to think they did it themselves. That feeling of accomplishment you just gave them is a direct gift. If as an adult you are helicoptered up to the top of Mount Kilimanjaro to see the view from above the clouds, it would be breathtaking of course, but it would not *feel* the same as if you'd hauled your beautiful bottom up that mountain over nine gruelling days to see it. Triumph cannot exist without struggle preceding it. Our hope for you is that you can learn to sit peacefully alongside your child's struggle, allowing them the golden opportunity that can only arise when struggle isn't stifled.

Healthy separation

Learning to sleep independently is just one of many things our children will need to learn to do at some point if they are to feel safe and secure when it comes to sleep. Take crawling as an example. It's considered the first form of independent movement. It helps develop and enhance a baby's vestibular/balance system, sensory system, cognition, problem-solving skills and coordination. Yet it is not always easy to watch a baby struggle to learn to crawl. Tummy time was recommended when I was a young mum. That is, allowing my daughter to struggle a little on her front, however much she didn't like it, because it was good for her.

There is an argument that sleep is not something to be taught. That it is just something that happens, like crawling. And I completely agree. Just as most babies are innately able to crawl, they are also innately able to sleep. What we don't tend to do as parents, when our babies are learning to crawl, is rush over and move them out of that position, taking away their opportunity to learn the skill. What we *do* do as parents, perhaps as a result of some of the gross misinformation out there about how highly responsive we must be at all times, is to rush in and rescue our babies as they are practising falling asleep independently. In doing so we inadvertently and unknowingly rob them of the opportunity to do something that they are perfectly capable of doing themselves. This is why you will often find that second, third and fourth babies will sleep better – their parents are not able to rush in and intervene as easily as they would have for their first child when there were fewer distractions around. In not being able to intervene, they provide their children with a magical opportunity to do their thing.

For us, the truth is that love is just as much about letting our children go as it is about holding them close. Within minutes of being born, the cord that joins a mother and a baby is cut. It is the first severance in the name of independence. The first separation on a long road of many more. At almost every stage of our child's life we teach them to survive without us. We teach them to eat and drink, to walk, talk, climb, swim, learn, drive and be without us. Healthy separation is such an intrinsic part of loving a child. We love them so much that we give them the tools to live without us.

What if it doesn't work?

One of the key questions I had before I decided to make what turned out to be the best parenting decision I ever made was, 'What if it doesn't work?' All the misinformed material I'd read had led me to believe that sleep teaching was not only harmful, but that it wasn't even effective. And that if it was, it wouldn't last. I now know this to be about as far from the truth as possible. Countless studies have used a variety of procedures (many of them randomised) to strongly support the argument that sleep teaching is effective and incredibly beneficial. A 2006 review of nineteen sleep-training studies showed that sleep improved in seventeen of the studies.[7] This review considered more than 2500 children. Another fourteen studies all showed improvement. Other studies showed the results of sleep teaching with the parent present in the room. Every one of these had improvements too. The findings of the review, appointed by the American Academy of Sleep Medicine, stated that sleep teaching produced reliable and durable changes. Across all fifty-two studies, 94 per cent reported as effective, with over 80 per cent of children demonstrating a significant improvement to their sleep. These positive effects on sleep last beyond the six to twelve months mark, too. Children who are sleep taught are sleeping better at least a year on. In short, there is an enormous amount of evidence to suggest that sleep teaching is effective in improving sleep. Further to the documented evidence, our team has witnessed thousands of families turn their life around thanks to effectiveness of sleep teaching the C&B way. The vast majority of families witness a change within three to five days and the benefits are quite literally endless. Furthermore, this is sleep that lasts for years and years to come. We can't wait to for you to meet just a handful of C&B families in the next chapter.

CHAPTER FIVE

THE HARD-HITTING
TRUTH ABOUT SLEEP

A hard pill to swallow

We want to begin this chapter with a gentle warning. If you're a tired parent, you might find this part of the book the hardest to digest. We know first-hand how triggering it can be to be told what sleep loss does to the body and mind. But tell you we must, and we will not sugarcoat it. For it is high time that the parents of the world had the data-driven facts at their fingertips. We can't promise you that what we have to say will be comfortable to hear – we all know that the truth can be a hard pill to swallow at times. What we can do is help you wash it down with a refreshing dose of hope, which we'll give you in abundance at the end of this chapter.

Eve's story

My first encounter with the hard-hitting facts about sleep came during my 465th frantic Google cry for help. I typed in to the search bar, '*Can you die from a lack of sleep?*' at the ungodly hour of four something, one bleak and desperate morning. As the screen produced page after page of data on the impact of poor sleep on the human body and mind. I scan-read what I could until morning; my eyes weary but widened in disbelief, my jaw gaping. It was impossible to take it all in, but a choice few facts stuck in my mind and have never left. One of those was the discovery that rats either die (or sacrifice themselves in anticipation of death) after just *eleven days* of no sleep.[8] That fact alone slapped me round the face and set alight in me an insatiable interest in sleep and how a lack of it affects our brains and bodies. Since that fateful day I have learnt things that I'd like to unlearn, such as the fact that routinely sleeping less than six or seven hours a night more than doubles your risk of cancer.[9] Despite it being my job to help families harness sleep, I'd almost rather not know that high blood pressure, obesity, diabetes, heart attack and stroke are more likely in sleep-deprived adults. Or that not enough sleep is a key factor in determining whether we develop Alzheimer's disease.[10] Part of me would like to be blissfully unaware that women who work night shifts are at a 40 per cent increased risk of developing breast cancer and that thirty-eight Danish night-shift-working women were recently awarded compensation in acknowledgment of the link between their disrupted sleep patterns and breast cancer.[11] It was disquieting to discover that an increase in teenage suicidal behaviour can be predicted by sleep disturbances[12] and that tiredness has played a part in some of the world's greatest disasters, such as the nuclear power plant tragedy at Chernobyl.[13]

Not only is it harder to concentrate and react without sleep (essential for the safe care of raising children), but we also can't form or maintain the brain pathways needed to learn and create new memories. Sleep is critical to a number of brain functions such as how nerve cells (neurons) communicate with each other. Recent findings from the National Institute of Neurological Disorders and Stroke suggests that sleep removes damaging toxins associated with brain degeneration.[14] Sleep loss is linked with depression, anxiety, bipolar disorder and other mental health conditions. Sleep affects every single fibre and function in the body – from the brain, heart and lungs to metabolism, immune function, mood and disease resistance. The Mental Health Foundation recently deemed sleep 'as important to our physical and mental health as eating, drinking and breathing'.[15] Ultimately it is as essential to survival as food and water. With that in mind, is sleep really something you want your children to go without?

How much sleep do we need?

Before we look at what a lack of sleep does, let's clear up what 'adequate' sleep is, shall we? Most adults need seven to eight hours a night.[16] You might be surprised to find out that chronically sleep-deprived people are termed as people routinely getting less than seven hours of sleep a night! But, before your head goes into a spin (as ours did when we discovered this), remember that a certain amount of sleep disruption is entirely *normal and expected* in the first half year of a baby's life. Even beyond that, sleep can be momentarily disturbed by fleeting threats to sleep such as teething, illness, developmental changes and emotional rocks to the boat such as the arrival of a new baby, a start at a new childcare setting, a house move or a holiday. We simply must recognise that *some* broken sleep is part and parcel of being either a small human or a parent of one. Broken sleep at the beginning of each child's life is completely natural and just how it is meant to be. There is nothing wrong, nor is there anything to be fixed.

But accepting that the beginning of parenting brings seriously shady sleep doesn't mean we need to lie down and surrender to it for weeks, months and years beyond that. While you have every right to walk the less-rested path, the newsflash is that *you do not have to.*

The benefits of sleep teaching for adults

While the focus of popular discussion on sleep teaching is on its supposed harms, the academic literature largely focuses on its merit. This is the case not only for infants but also for the parents. Adults who continually sleep less than seven hours a night experience a devastating impact on their immune system and gut microbiome; a key system which we now know plays a pivotal role in our overall health and well-being. Insufficient sleep makes us more susceptible to diabetes, infertility, obesity and cardiovascular disease. Indeed, the need for sleep lives at the very life-source of a human; without sleep, even our hearts cannot operate at optimum condition.

The dangers are not only slow burning, though. Each year in the UK, fatigue-induced car crashes outweigh those caused by drink and drugs combined, with an estimated 30 per cent of fatalities down to tiredness. In America, someone dies every hour from a fatigue-related car crash, with 1.2 million accidents caused by sleepiness each year. Four hours or less of sleep increases your chances of a car crash by 11.5 times.[17] Chronically tired parents in their millions are driving their most precious cargo around, unaware that they could be just as impaired as if they were drunk.

Perhaps the most compelling argument for sleep teaching from a parents' perspective is how effective it is at reducing maternal depression. One Australian study split 328 children into two groups, one which was sleep-trained and the other not. Two and four months later, the mothers in the sleep-trained group were less depressed and had better physical health.[18] The studies consistently show that sleep teaching is beneficial for parental mental health. Parents who sleep teach their children are happier in their marriages, less depressed and find parenting less stressful. One study showed a striking effect of sleep teaching on maternal mental health; 70 per cent of mothers in the group fitted the criteria for clinical depression at the start of the trial, and only 10 per cent after sleep teaching.[19] If the UK figures on maternal depression are considered, this could potentially mean that up to 72,000 mothers a year could be freed from the grip of maternal depression if only they got the rest they needed.

Maternal depression is a recognised risk for adverse child development. Two thirds of clinically significant depressive symptoms occur in mothers reporting an infant sleep problem.[20] Some of the most jaw-dropping results came from a study which measured the long-term effects of sleep teaching on maternal depression and parenting style, as well as on child mental health and sleep. The children in the study were aged two. It found that sleep teaching had a positive impact on maternal depression. Furthermore, it found no evidence of longer-term adverse effects on any of the mothers' parenting practices or on the children's mental health. This study expertly demonstrated how much change sleep interventions can make for the better, preventing families from succumbing to the grip of sleep deprivation a second time once they have the tools in place to enable the best possible sleep.

For many parents, a show-stopping concern is that sleep teaching will adversely affect the mental health of the child or the parent. Yet the evidence on this is clear; infant security and attachment *increases* after sleep teaching. A recent study looked at the effects of controlled comforting on infant sleep, stress, later child emotional and behavioural problems and parent stress.[21] The researchers also measured the infant and the mother's cortisol levels by testing their saliva. They did this at the time of the sleep teaching and again three months later. The infants who were sleep taught not only slept better but the cortisol levels of both the infants and their mothers *reduced*, representing less stress for both. The findings concluded that sleep teaching does not impact on child–parent attachment either at the time or twelve months later. At a follow-up one year on, there were no differences between the studied groups in child emotional and behavioural problems or in secure/insecure parent–child attachment (these factors measured by the universally accepted gold standard 'Strange Situation' test). This study offers us the most concrete evidence yet that sleep interventions such as controlled crying cause no short-term or long-term harm as measured by infant cortisol and validated ratings of child emotional and behavioural symptoms and parent–child attachment.

The bond between parent and child wasn't all that was positively impacted by sleep intervention. Improvements in appetite and eating and daytime behaviour was also reported by the parents. A 2006 review of sleep-training studies noted:

Adverse secondary effects as the result of participating in behaviourally based sleep programs were not identified in any of the studies. On the contrary, infants were found to be more secure, predictable, less irritable, and to cry and fuss less.[22]

A Surgeon on Sleep: Doctor Jenna Rao, NHS Surgeon

When my daughter was six months old, I was still feeding to sleep and she would be awake for an hour and a half each time she woke. But if I accidentally woke her when putting her into the cot, that meant another forty-five minutes minimum of feeding to put her back to sleep . . . I was exhausted.

The day we contacted Eve for help, we had gone out for lunch and I had broken down in tears in the restaurant in front of all of our friends, begging my husband to 'fix it!' because I was simply too tired to function. I was due back at work in a couple of months (as a surgeon) and had no idea how I would manage to drive to work, let alone operate, on so little sleep.

I had the recommendation of Calm & Bright from a friend from medical school so decided to ring for a chat. I can honestly say it was the best decision I have made as a parent and my daughter is now five years old! Within two days she was sleeping eleven hours overnight with two two-hour naps (previously her record was only forty minutes during the daytime!).

We never looked back and Lyla has been an excellent sleeper ever since. Eve's 'future-proofing' meant we also knew what to do about dropping her naps, we fixed her early waking and when my son was born, he was already sleeping eight hours overnight by the time he was eight weeks old! If anyone is considering sleep training, I cannot recommend Eve or Calm & Bright more highly. She supported me through it all and helped me to teach my babies one of life's most valuable skills – solid sleep!

CHAPTER SIX

WHY DO WE ACCEPT BAD SLEEP?

Deep within society, there is a fearful, submissive groan which will warn you that this kind of sleep isn't real and can't be achieved, and that even if it could, it won't last. It will encourage you to struggle on, wearing your exhaustion like a badge of honour. It will tell you that you don't have the energy to sort sleep out. That the reason your child doesn't sleep is because they're not *meant* to. It'll have you believe that it's natural for them to endlessly wake through the night, well into their third year, and for you to see to those calls as if they were still a newborn. It'll make you think that seeking better sleep is selfish and indulgent. A product of the modern world. You'll come to believe that it is your duty to be on call twenty-four hours a day to meet your baby's needs, even if it costs you your sanity.

Where did these ideas come from?

The anti-sleep-teaching movement has a number of different roots, which we're going to explore with you now. One of those roots can be traced back to the introduction of attachment theory in 1950s England. This theory, which highlighted the critical importance of the emotional bond between parent and child, arose thanks to the work of psychoanalyst John Bowlby and, later, researcher Mary Ainsworth. It revealed that disruption to – or loss of – a secure emotional parent–child bond can affect a child emotionally and psychologically into adulthood. Thankfully, this movement opened the world's eyes to just how critical the first years of a child's life are.

Reconsidering attachment theory

It has recently been argued that the evidence Bowlby based his theory on was thin; based not so much on science as on a mixture of personal and cultural biases. These included his own childhood. One of six children, Bowlby was cared for by nurses on a different floor of the family's lavish home. He spent just an hour each day with his mother, and saw his father only once a week. His favourite nanny left when he was four. At age seven, he was sent to a boarding school. He spoke openly about the impact his childhood lack of attachment had on him as an adult.

Dr Jerome Kagan, a Professor Emeritus at Harvard University who is listed by the American Psychological Association as the twenty-second most eminent psychologist of the twentieth century.[23] He deems Bowlby's suggestion, that what happens in the first year of life influences how you'll be for the rest of your life, as 'an unreasonable idea'. What makes the theory problematic is that it doesn't take into account the profound influences of gender, class, ethnicity and society/culture on how a child develops.

Another problem with attachment theory is the insistence that the more you give to your child, the better they will turn out. We'd urge any parent to consider whether *giving everything* is worth the price of *losing it*. Rather than frantically trying to fill up our child's cup with our own empty dregs, we might choose instead to give ourselves time to refill our *own* cup. When we do this – through whatever makes us feel good, such as exercise, other relationships, practices that give us clarity of mind and softness of heart – our children benefit immeasurably. When we live our life connected to our authentic truth, in line with what brings us joy and peace, we not only give our children the gift of a happy mother, we give them permission to do the same. Is there a greater lesson to teach our children than that?

A Counsellor on Sleep: Felicity Dutton, Integrative Therapist, MBACP

When we are at our best, we are able to offer our children our best in return. By our 'best' I don't of course mean being the perfect mum; you will hopefully know by now that good enough is more than enough! Instead, I mean our children can look into our eyes and see love, joy, hope and wonder. Not the strained stare of dread and resentment that sleep deprivation brings. All adults need somewhere between seven to nine hours of sleep a night for optimum physical and mental health. When we consistently have less than that, the physical and mental toll can greatly impact our well-being, judgement and even our sense of reality. Lack of sleep can lead to and exasperate depression and anxiety, two foes that already threaten our experience of motherhood. Extreme tiredness robs us of enjoying time and making memories with our children. When we get the sleep we need, the whole family benefits physically and mentally. All too often a mum pours all her energy and resources into her family and thinks about what she needs later. Imagine what a gift it would be to teach our children the importance of taking care of themselves by taking care of ourselves and what better place to start than with the restorative wonder that is sleep?

It isn't only Bowlby's controversial science that has been placed under the microscope in recent times. Paediatrician William Sears is perhaps one of the most famous proponents of attachment theory. One of the central warnings in his work is that babies who cry too much could suffer permanent brain damage, leading to a lower IQ, behavioural problems and more. To evidence his claims, he explains that the stress hormone cortisol floods the body during times of distress, preventing brain cells from making healthy connections and leading to developmental and cognitive delay. Rather problematically, two of the four studies he cites as his evidence were conducted on rat pups and one was in a group of non-human primates. The one study that did involve human babies was a German study of seventy babies in their first few months in day care. Unsurprisingly, the babies were already experiencing increased stress because of their new-found separation from the mother. Furthermore, three of the studies on crying used babies who were already suffering from colic or 'persistent crying', which resulted in inconsolable crying despite parental soothing. Once more, this study is completely out of context when considering lovingly attended-to upset in otherwise healthy babies.

The role of patriarchy

It's important to note that the idea of attachment came right after the Second World War, when the world had a keen interest in psychological trauma and when parents were reacting to the rigidity of their own upbringing. The world was also at peace, a luxury which gave it the opportunity to ask important questions such as what a happy and successful life looked like. Bowlby's answer – that if a mother is loving, affectionate and consistent in the first year or two of life then the child will forever be protected from things like anxiety and depression – was keenly received. This was in part because it appealed to fears about women going to work. Young mothers were entering the workforce in huge numbers and needed to find childcare to make this possible. In 1960s America, as mothers began working outside of the home, news articles in Europe and America warned that it would have dire consequences. The protests against women working were so powerful that they delayed the launch of national day care centres in America. The notion that what a mother does during the first few years of her child's life either makes or breaks that child kept women conveniently at home, too occupied (and possibly too tired) to question the men who had decided how they should live their lives.

There can be no reasonable doubt that severe neglect or abuse of children during the first few years of life can harm them psychologically in the future. What is important to note is that sleep teaching doesn't involve severe – or for that matter mild – neglect or abuse. On the contrary, the research speaks clearly when it tells us that sleep teaching does the opposite of what it is accused of. It *strengthens* attachment, *enhances* familial bonds, *improves* maternal mental health, *reduces* stress and gives each child the parent they deserve, one rested enough to witness and share the wonder of the world we live in.

Kate's story

Kate reached out to us in a state of total shame. The wife of a GP, she had been diagnosed with breast cancer while pregnant with her first baby. She had some incredibly difficult decisions to make about her pregnancy and treatment and decided to postpone treatment until her baby was safely in her arms. Shortly after the birth of her son she started her life-saving treatment. She'd been advised by her medical team to stop breastfeeding and move her baby onto formula because the chemotherapy wasn't safe for her baby and she needed to spend some time away from him for treatment. As Kate went into remission, she recalled feeling utter joy that the nightmare was over. But just as she began to find her feet and navigate her new normal, she found herself drowning in feelings of shame and deep disappointment. Being forced to separate from her baby, Kate felt as if she'd been robbed of the precious early weeks and not being able to breastfeed – something she'd dreamt of doing from the beginning – left her steeped in guilt. Kate turned to a well-known attachment parenting and breastfeeding advocate for reassurance and advice. Heartbreakingly, she was told that she had made a huge mistake by formula-feeding her son. She was told that she should have fed him with donated expressed milk from a milk bank instead of letting him be 'subjected to' formula. Kate told us that she'd never felt so ashamed and alone. In seeking support, she had put her trust in someone to support her and she was met with hostility and judgement. In Kate's own words, the wrath and abuse she received was too much for her fragile heart to bear. At a time when she was searching for a lifeline, for some reprieve from the all-consuming guilt she felt, she was met with criticism for the choices she had made to enable her to survive. Kate told us that it took her months to summon the courage to reach out for help again. She said she typed the message out to send to us six times. Terrified to press send for fear of getting another cruel response. Instead, what she received from Gem was a teary voice note, listening ears and all the support she longed for. Kate never needed a plan in the end, but she tells us that our communication helped her to put to rest some of those awful feelings, which meant that our work was done! Thank you, Kate, for letting us be a small part of your journey and for allowing us to tell your story to speak your truth. You are brave beyond measure.

The need to be heard and seen

We understand that when a parent is on their knees, like Kate, they need to be heard and seen, fast. They cannot wait a moment longer. If once they've shared their story, they're told to carry on living alongside their broken sleep, it denies them their truth. When despair is met with dismissal, parents end up taking their feelings back inside themselves. As Felicity Dutton, C&B integrative thera-pist explains:

'When we reach out for help, we usually have to put aside some deep-rooted thoughts and feelings about ourselves. Some of these might be "I shouldn't need help", "I should be able to cope better" and "Why can't I do this myself?". When this plea for support is met with dismissal or denial, our problem is made to feel inconsequential, an overreaction or not a big deal. This can leave us feeling emotionally bruised and very reluctant to reach out again. It also reinforces the very feelings we had to fight through in the first place in order to ask for the help and relief we were so desperately seeking.'

Unheard feelings

Unheard feelings as strong as these don't just waft away into thin air. As we know too well, what goes in must come out! Unexpressed desperation materialises in resentment, bitterness and hostility. Left unacknowledged, despair festers, multiplies and pollutes. This can often be seen and felt in our dealings with the ones we love the most. Eve doesn't mind telling you that she once fantasised about jabbing her husband between the eyes with a kebab skewer!! Thankfully, through our work, she knew that intrusive, distressing thoughts are part of what it means to be human. Throw exhaustion into the mix and we can easily see how these kinds of feelings can spill out. Mothers in their millions have taken their own resentments and regret out on the ones they love. They need to be supported to find freedom from the source of the difficulty (dangerously low levels of sleep), not berated for it and told to carry on. Sadly, stories like Kate's are not unusual. Women so often tell us that they have been shamed, called out, attacked, pressurised and interrogated by those against sleep teaching. They tell us that their experience of some members of the supposedly nurturing attachment community was in fact spiked with aggression, hostility and scare-mongering.

Sally's story

When I reached out, we'd spent the last two years averaging five to six hours of sleep a night with three to four wake-ups for a feed from our two year old. I was a staunch attachment parent who thought that sleep training was the stuff of the devil. I'd reached for the most popular sleep training book of the time and felt panicked as I skim read it; it felt so alien to me. 'Put your baby on a cold surface to wake them up . . . ' WHAT?! There was no warmth and no love. I then basically did the classic thing of 'use the internet to find people on your side and to prove your own argument' and quickly I found people saying that sleep training is money-making, that the books are written by nannies who don't have kids, that being a parent is hard and just get on with it, that babies aren't meant to sleep, blah blah blah. 'YES' I thought! Yes! When a lovely friend sent me the details for Calm & Bright, I politely said thanks while silently rolling my eyes, thinking '*Oh great – another company who can teach me how to ignore my kids!*'

But then I started reading their posts and watching their reels and thought HANG ON . . . these ladies are the Miss Honeys of baby sleep?! I actually LIKED them, they were real parents, so warm, loving and kind but also looked like great fun and not too sickly sweet. Within a few days all my preconceived ideas of sleep training as cruel were blown out the water. Eve and Gem seemed like the type of mums I wanted my daughter to have.

Before we got started, naps were a disaster too; any attempt to get her to nap involved me lying with her, which got me so frustrated, as in my mind I could see the list of jobs I had to do. Forty-five minutes in, I'd give up and we'd both carry on, exhausted. It's kind of heartbreaking to consider how challenging life was before we enabled sleep. The tantrums were off the scale. I had to deal with her emotions (which she found impossible to regulate on the amount of sleep she was getting) and I couldn't regulate mine either, so it was a vicious circle.

Every night now, I kiss her good night and SHE GOES TO SLEEP HAPPILY BY HERSELF!!! Seriously, you have no idea how clingy and boob-dependent she was. I honestly thought this wouldn't happen until she was about seven years old! The other miracle is that she goes down better for hubby than me! I had two and a half years of it only being me who could put her to bed!

I feel like I've got my little girl back, like she has her mummy back and that my husband has his wife back! The difference is absolutely huge. She is a gorgeous firecracker, so still has the odd tantrum, but when she does, I can deliver empathy and calm rather than exploding. Not only am I no longer the shouty mum but I've started to shed some weight and get back into exercise and feel more energised. My husband and I LAUGH together again and even have actual conversations with real sentences and words rather than grunting at each other with a few death stares over who had the most sleep. I have a glorious skin routine now that it's less about crawling into bed like a ninja and more about having several hours between my children's bedtime and my own!

I cannot express how anti sleep training I was. I literally pictured the silent orphans in Romania who didn't cry as they knew no one would come. I tortured myself reading how their brains are flooded with cortisol still even though they don't cry . . . if ONLY I'd busted these myths sooner!! The thing which struck a chord was how many times a day my daughter was having meltdowns – and how those were the times when her brain was flooded with cortisol! It wasn't until I was rested that I could see that I had unknowingly been depriving us both of sleep and that was more negligent of her needs than the sleep training.

The C&B sleep teaching is done with such love. You are there with them, you are listening in and you are reassuring them. The results are gobsmacking! I don't believe there is a better gift to give your child and yourself than sleep.

Ten untruths a tired parent is told:

1. It's 'just how it is' and you are powerless to change it

2. Babies aren't meant to sleep

3. It's biologically normal for children to wake up overnight (without explaining that your presence isn't needed each time)

4. It may be several years before you sleep again

5. Your baby is only young once so enjoy it while you can

6. You can sleep when the baby sleeps

7. Sleep training is neglectful and unloving

8. Your child will be damaged if you allow them a moment's upset

9. They will only stop crying because they have given up hope

10. Even if sleep training works, you'll have to sleep train again and again as it won't last

Ten truths a tired parent should be told:

1. Long-term exhaustion is intolerable and unsustainable for any human being – how well your baby sleeps is not a reflection on you

2. It is normal to feel intense rage and emotional volatility when depleted

3. Taking difficult feelings out on the ones we love happens

4. It is not weak to know how to sort sleep, it is normal

5. You do not have to cope on too little sleep for too long

6. Millions of others feel the same but have had their feelings silenced

7. It is courageous and smart to seek professional help with anything, sleep included

8. There is definite and positive action that can be taken to turn sleep around

9. There is an unlimited abundance of compassionate, love-led support in place to help and support you

CHAPTER SEVEN

THE IMPORTANCE OF SLEEP

The importance of sleep in babies and young children

The human need for sleep doesn't just begin at the click of a finger as a person turns eighteen. Sleep plays a key role from the very beginning of human existence. Most of a foetus's time in utero is spent asleep. In the last trimester, there's an unprecedented peak in the amount of REM sleep the foetus takes in preparation for the most gruelling task a human will ever face.[24] The week before birth marks the highest peak of REM sleep that a human will *ever* take. This need for REM sleep dominates early developmental life, when the brain is undergoing the greatest neurological development. During the transition from newborn to childhood, sleep is one of the primary activities of the brain. It plays a vital role in early brain development, particularly on learning and memory and emotional regulation in the early years.[25]

Studies show that ten-month-old babies who sleep soundly at night have an easier temperament and are more approachable and adaptable.[26] On the other hand, babies who get less sleep have more difficulty with emotional regulation. Rested babies separate from their caregivers more happily. In a study of well-rested and not so well-rested babies, the tired group were more easily frustrated and more distressed by a brief separation from their mothers. In multiple studies of interventions that improved infants' sleep, parents noted that their babies were more secure, predictable, less irritable, and less fussy. There has recently been a call for sleep to be taken into account in the consideration of developmental delay or behaviour problems, particularly in the first year of life.[27]

Having enough good-quality sleep is a key – and often under-estimated – protective factor for children, helping them to regenerate their brains and bodies, to process information and memories, boost immunity, guard against obesity, and help concentration, learning and behaviour.

As we were writing this section of the book, one mum got in touch with us to tell us about her daughter who was getting just six to eight hours of broken sleep a night when she started school in September last year. Her daughter's teacher used to phone them throughout the day to tell them that their daughter was struggling, but she felt helpless to change it. Not only was it taking hours to get her daughter to sleep, she was then waking every few hours and experiencing night terrors. She had a food allergy and had been diagnosed with a sleep disorder. This family was four and a half years in to disturbed sleep which nearly broke them mentally, physically and as a couple. In this mum's own words, 'It cost us friendships, our health and at times our sanity.' This family was at breaking point. Despite being sure that they were beyond help, they knew that they could no longer survive and so purchased the plan with 'extremely low expectations'. They hoped that it might just help with getting their evenings back so that they could deal with the disturbed nights. Four nights into following our plan and this little girl began sleeping twelve hours a night. Virtually overnight, she stopped having night terrors. The little girl is now thriving at school and her teacher can't believe the difference. This family is now five months in to solid sleep and life is for ever changed.

A headteacher on Sleep: Alanda Phillips, Headteacher of Leweston Prep, Dorset

Slumping on the desks and yawning loudly are far from the only effects of a lack of sleep that teachers see each day. Over fifteen years of teaching, with the last five as a headteacher, I have seen hundreds of children consistently held back from reaching their potential because they are just too tired. A tired child arrives at school without the drive and determination needed to succeed; they lack clarity of thought as their exhausted brain swims through problems, and before long they just give up. In our five-year-olds, we see this largely exemplified in those children who fail to settle into school life, and who suffer emotional outbursts and cannot negotiate relationships effectively. Working alongside parents, we often establish that broken sleep, or insufficient sleep, might be at the root, and invariably an improvement in sleep pattern and timing directly leads to better emotional stability.

A child who has had a good night's sleep arrives at school settled, happy and ready to learn. They develop the necessary resilience to 'bounce back' when they experience difficulties, and they are able to compromise, communicate and generally build and maintain relationships far more effectively. It is hard to over-state the impact that high-quality sleep has in all aspects of your child's development in a school environment, without even touching on the benefits to family life that you will experience at home.

By the age of ten, we see a long-term impact. A lifetime of broken sleep and early exhaustion leaves them demotivated; failing to meet the expectations that were held for them in their early years. As bedtimes steadily creep later, and the pre-teen hormones take hold, we see them not only profoundly affected academically, but also witness the lack of emotional resilience that they need to handle the changes ahead of them. If teachers could be met with classes of well-rested children, there is no doubt that progress levels across the country would rise, but more than that, we would be one step closer to supporting the development of a happy, resilient generation. I implore you to ensure that your child is one of those.

Sleep associations ('the ings')

Sleep happens in four distinct phases, which we cycle through several times a night. The first three phases take us from light to deeper sleep (NREM phases 1–3) while the fourth phase, REM sleep, is where our deepest sleep takes place. The whole cycle takes between thirty and 120 minutes, depending on how old we are and how we are programmed. So our little ones are meant to come into light sleep several times a night. It's what we do when they wake – and just before they sleep – that defines whether they will sleep their best sleep.

We refer to *the ings* as anything your child depends on to get to – or get back to – sleep. We call them *the ings* because the words usually end with an *ing*: feeding, rocking, staying, patting, stroking, co-sleeping, sucking (dummy), handholding or moving (sling, pram, car sleep). Let's be abundantly clear here: there is nothing wrong with the ings. They are the very lifelines most parents depend upon at first and their origins lie in the early days of tender soothing. The only time the ings become a problem for parents is when they stop working; when they go from feeling like magic to more of a curse.

Self-soothing

We were absolutely gobsmacked to read the *Oxford English Dictionary*'s definition of self-soothing:

Noun
The action of a young child ceasing to cry without being comforted by a parent or carer, in particular when left to fall asleep on their own.
'in order to encourage self-soothing parents can provide baby with a consistent night-time ritual'

Adjective
(of a young child) able to stop crying without being comforted by a parent or carer, in particular when being left to fall asleep on their own.
'self-soothing babies generally sleep longer each night'

For us, this couldn't be further from the truth. Self-soothing involves *no crying* and looks like a baby being placed in their cot or bed and falling peacefully asleep. A baby who can self-settle does so by feeling so emotionally secure and confident of their parental attachment, that they can self-settle. That security and attachment comes from babies feeling *so* secure and beautifully attached to their parent that that very extension of love and enablement means that even if the parent isn't physically present when the baby drifts off to sleep, they settle regardless. It is the epitome of a loved, securely attached baby. That's not to say there won't be some tears or protest as changes are made to *teach* self-soothing. But it's not the self-soothing that brings any upset. If it comes, upset happens in response to parents making changes to behaviours and patterns that weren't working for them or their child.

It's no wonder parents are feeling confused about what it means. Self-soothing is one of the greatest gifts you can give your child. It's love.

Self-soothing is heralded as the golden chalice of solid sleep for good reason. Either a child does sleep *themselves*, or a parent does it *for* them. This is determined by what happens as a child goes from wakefulness to sleep. Either they are taking themselves over that finish line, or they are being carried over it using one of *the ings*. Whatever way sleep repeatedly happens for your child, it sends a message to them (and you) that *this is how sleep happens*. When we rock or feed our baby to sleep each time, we tell them that *this is how they get to sleep*. This is how they get to sleep. This is how they get to sleep. This message is delivered consistently and over a long period of time. It's really no wonder that it sinks in and becomes a learned behaviour.

Let's take a ten-month-old baby who has always been fed to sleep. Now we'll be honest with you, we're not great at maths, but we reckon that they've received the message around a thousand times in their very short life that *this is how sleep is done*. That's a reliable and solid message right there! As time goes on, a child quite understandably and rightly concludes that this is the only way sleep happens. Their belief is reinforced and fortified each day. When we try to do sleep another way, our child understandably gets upset. This does not mean that they *can't* do sleep any other way, rather that that they don't yet know *how*. The longer a sleep association continues, the deeper that belief runs in the parent and child, and the more ingrained it becomes. Perhaps you can see how we the parents play the biggest role in whether a child sleeps their best sleep? This doesn't mean that your child's sleep is your *fault*, rather that it's within your *power* to turn it around.

Eve's story

I will never forget the time I found out the reason that my two-year-old had been pinching my cheeks. Ted was the youngest of my four children and for around a month he had been squeezing my face with each of his tiny hands. It was not only uncomfortable but it was also confusing. You see, he wasn't doing it in anger, as you might imagine. He did it whenever we were sitting quietly together in the way we always sat (and still sit now) with him astride my lap, face to face while I grabbed a moment's rest, often with his sweet head nuzzled into my neck. We always felt so inter-connected, so the pinching came as a shock. Over the weeks leading up to that day, Ted's pinching episodes had increased. I had no idea why my beautiful, gentle boy was hurting me on purpose. So, when he reached up his little face to mine and grabbed both my cheeks and pinched them that day, I said to him in exasperation 'Ted, it really hurts when you do that to Mummy! Why do you do it?' His eyes widened with surprise and he smiled at me, but with big eyes, because it was more for me than him. His reply broke my heart into a thousand tiny pieces.

'It's to help you smile, Mummy,' he said.

Knowing I was about to cry, and not wanting him to see the pain etched on my face, I pulled him in close and held him tight as the tears from my heart wet his shoulder. All that time I'd thought my gentle giant was becoming an aggressive toddler. The truth was that his heart was even bigger than I thought. As my tears flowed (there was no hiding them now), I realised that each time he squeezed my face it was because his knackered mummy's sadness was too much to bear. Perhaps it shouldn't have been such a surprise to me that he was so in tune with how hopeless I felt. I suppose I had hoped that my cheery veneer could mask the deep in my bones exhaustion that I felt almost every day in these early years of being a parent. But of course, I was wrong.

Exhausted parents are parenting at a huge disadvantage. I experienced this first-hand myself. I remember one of my children running down the stairs with glee to tell me how proud she was that she'd learned how to plait her doll's hair. All I was able to muster in response was a monotone voice that replied, 'That's wonderful, darling, how clever of you.' But my tone betrayed my lack of genuine connection with my daughter's pride. It was not that I was *not* proud of her. It was simply that I was too tired to properly *be* there. I was reserving every ounce of energy just to get through the relentless days and nights. The phrase 'running on empty' didn't even cut it – I was barely crawling.

We know that it can feel daunting to consider sleep on the grand scale that it deserves. Discovering just how critical sleep is for the human body and mind has the potential to make us feel guilty, especially if sleep hasn't been sound for some time. We know that guilt is a feeling that no parent needs an extra dose of. Parenthood is littered with far too much of that as it is. But we take our duty of care to you seriously and feel we should at least offer you access to the evidence-supported findings on the topic. What you do with the information is entirely up to you.

The good news we bring is that broken sleep doesn't need to be tolerated. It can be halted, turned around and transformed into something truly wonderful in no time at all. After just one good night of sleep, we can feel more hopeful, focused, positive, motivated and energised. Enough rest means we treat ourselves and the people we love with more care and compassion. We can remember to send that card on time. Or have enough energy to do the things that help us feel like we're winning. A rested parent can make decisions from a place of confidence and clarity. They feel better about themselves and are more emotionally available for the ones they love. All these things add up over time and life feels better.

The science speaks clearly and urgently. Sleep is a key, non-negotiable need. It is perhaps the most powerful elixir that the natural world has to offer us.

CHAPTER EIGHT

HOW TO MAKE SLEEP WORK FOR YOUR FAMILY

It's natural for parenting recommendations to evolve over time, but you'll be hard pushed to find anything that's changed more than the advice on sleep. Our dear mum told us how her generation were put to sleep in wooden drawers, and we ourselves were left to nap at the bottom of the snow-filled garden, so long as we were wrapped up 'good and proper'! Sleep advice is ever-changing and evolving, which it must as new information comes to light. But this makes it difficult for parents to get a grip on the current advice. This is where we come in. We are at your service, here to offer you the science and research-supported information (and our take on it based on our own experience) so that you can arrive fully armed with all the knowledge you need to make your own decisions about the path that feels best to you.

Routine

When parents reach out to us for support, one of the first things we get asked is about routine. What routine do we recommend at Calm & Bright? When should parents be getting their child into a routine? Are they too young? Too old? Whether your family's style is more go-with-the-flow or to-the-minute, the way you chose to do things should serve you best. A routine needn't be restrictive and it's so much less stressful when it isn't. Creating your day-to-day family life based around what works for you – and not what someone *tells* you should work for you – is really liberating. You get to design your days to build the life you want. Your routine can be flexible when it needs to be, or more planned out when required. Either way, it is there to make your life easier, not harder. We can tell you from personal experience that it can feel totally overwhelming to spend your days worrying about fitting the *right* amount of sleep into your day, while navigating nursery and school drop-offs for other children and stressing about danger naps. Parenthood is tough enough without putting pressure on yourself to adhere to an unrealistic routine. The secret here is to let the routine serve you, not the other way round. Know that it's ok if you need to break the rules or even make up your own. Going off-piste is part and parcel of everyday life.

On the other hand, if you want to run a tighter ship, that's cool too. We are very different when it comes to routine and what works for us in our families. Gem is more of a routine-Rita whereas Eve is more of a sail-with-the-wind Sally. Gem, being a typical nurse, is used to knowing what's what and loves a tidy, organised house. 3.5 children in, she's learning to let go of that a little bit, taking a leaf out of big sister's book and going with the flow a little more, and it's working. And in turn, Eve will call on her little sis from time to time to give her some guidance on routine and organisation when she feels in a bit of a spin. Hear us when we say that no matter what personality type you are or how you like to run your ship, you will find your own rhythm. The joy of our approach is that no matter where on the routine scale you sit, once settling is learnt, it's learnt. And that's true of a baby who is in a structured routine and one who isn't. It benefits all people in all ways.

Changes in routine

It's really normal for changes in routine caused by children going to a different childcare setting to breed anxiety in parents. We understand that it can feel difficult when sleep is out of your hands. It can feel especially tough when we're worried about the threat the change may cause to sleep (both our child's and our own). Of course, there will be times when sleep is broken, that's life. But once you have the tools that you need to enable self-settling, you'll find a way to do sleep in a different way to match your new set-up.

An example of this was when Eve's daughter Sena was five months old. Sena was in a nice little routine of having an epic two-hour nap from nine to eleven a.m. during the six-week school summer holidays. When school started up again and Eve's older two had to be taken to school at Sena's nap time, Eve's first instinct was sheer panic. She would have to do the school run in the middle of this crucial sleep that she'd pinned her whole day around! Sena's nap was when she washed, got the dinner on and rested herself. What if Sena fell asleep in the car and wouldn't transfer? What if she had a small sleep en route and wouldn't sleep again later? What about Eve's only time to herself each day? What if the change broke the good sleep in the night?

Let it go

Parenthood is gruelling at times and that heaven-sent time when your baby naps is not only super important for them and their development, it's also a sacred time for you to catch your breath, even for a moment. Time for you to pause, to grab a shower or put your feet up. Maybe even drink a drink while it's hot. So that dreaded anxiety you have about nap time being interrupted or sabotaged is a valid worry. But it's important to remember that you're not alone in having these worries and anxieties. Parents all over the world face the same fears and concerns, year on year. Eve had to have a little word with herself when she found herself fearing the worst when it came to Sena's nap and the school run, and it went something along the lines of this: 'You're not the only one who has more than one child trying to navigate all of this, Eve. Of course, it's inconvenient and really annoying, but you can make this work.' Eve did indeed make it work by forcing herself to relax about it, by being flexible and adapting to her new situation. Her relaxed attitude paid off. She simply adapted nap time so that Sena took fifteen minutes before the school run began (which was actually really helpful getting the elder two out the door). Those cheeky fifteen minutes meant that Sena stayed awake on the school run and then went on to have a whopper of a two-and-a-half-hour nap at what turned out to be an even better time for Eve than it was in the first place. This taught Eve that while she thought everything was clearer in black and white, there was a great deal to be said for the grey.

Sleep on the go

Don't worry if the time comes when sleep needs to happen out of the house. Spoiler alert: it will. Your child is going to know the difference between being at home for sleep and being somewhere else. That is also true of children that are in different childcare settings or who are being cared for by somebody else other than Mum and Dad. It's ok if sleep is done a different way in a different place. And even at a different time. You may find that the nap is longer, because there is more going on. Or that they take a shorter nap there than at home. Also ok. Parents often ask us how they can 'hand over' their child's nap routine to their childcare setting or family member looking after their child. Our response is always the same. As hard as it might be to get your head around, we think the path of least resistance for you, your baby and the ones caring for them is to accept that you have little or no control over day sleep on the days that your child isn't in your care. You might find that they take less or no sleep there, or they might sleep just fine (or better) when they're not with you. If sleep is less good away from home (something most parents find) then it may be that home days are catch-up days, and that away from home days need an early bedtime or a catch-up sleep the next day might be necessary.

It's very much a suck it and see approach that's needed. Sleep outside the home is not something you can prepare for. One thing of certainty is that you will find your own way to work through it and find a way that works for you. Try to remember that success will come from being adaptable to and relaxed about change to the sleep set-up. Have faith in your own ability to work it out!

Pandemic parenting

We are writing this book through a global pandemic, one that has affected every person in the world to some degree. It seems that mothers may have borne the brunt of the changes. The additional demands have made an already difficult job feel impossible for many mothers. With everyone at home more than ever, the amount of domestic chores, cooking and childcare has soared to an un-precedented high. This, coupled with having to be all things to all people at once – the parent, the teacher, the cleaner, the cook, the mediator and everything in between – has been a recipe for disaster for most mothers. A Mumsnet survey of 1500 mothers found that 79 per cent of them said that the responsibility for home schooling fell largely to them and 77 per cent agreed that it was impossible to work uninterrupted when schools closed.[28] A recent study from the Trades Union Congress found that nine out of ten working mothers said their mental health had been negatively affected by school closures.[29] Before the pandemic, one in five mums and one in ten dads reported experiencing perinatal mental health problems. The uncertainty of the virus and the social isolation it has imposed has made a stark impact on what is already an isolating and lonely time of life. According to the Institute of Health Visiting, in some areas of England at least 50 per cent of the United Kingdom's health visitors – including staff from perinatal mental health teams – were redeployed into other health services in the initial period of the lockdown. Mothers tell us that they are feeling more isolated than ever as they attempt to cope with the impact of COVID-19, the increased pressures due to a lack of childcare, social interaction and support resources. Pregnant women and new parents all over the world are having to manage one of life's most profound periods of transition in the midst of an international health crisis. It's a tall order indeed.

As we emerge from the national lockdown, with restrictions lifting as we speak (it is May 2021 at the time of writing) we are being contacted now more than ever by parents who are anxious about breaking their routine and doing sleep out and about. The restriction that was imposed upon us has become a bit of a security blanket. Babies under two years old will have got very used to sleeping at home, and so have their parents. This has generated a huge amount of anxiety. If you are experiencing any anxiety around changing your routine or doing sleep out and about, we encourage you to try to take the pressure off completely. Let your baby or child sleep when and where they want. Do not worry about them breaking their decent sleep. They are so much more adaptable than you think. The more relaxed about everything you are, the more relaxed they will be. Eve always enjoys telling the story of how her two-year-old fell asleep on the hard, cold floor of the school hall under a trestle table as she helped at one of her children's Christmas fayres one year. Ted's nap was due about an hour before, but he was having such a whale of a time with the other children there that instead of trying to create stress by imposing a nap at the *right* time, Eve let him whizz around until Ted's batteries ran down. When he finally came and nestled his head into her neck, she popped one coat on the floor, one coat on top of him and he was asleep within seconds. Despite the hall bellowing with Christmas cheer, high spirits and laughter, Ted didn't wake until two hours later when the last of the tidying up had been completed. This was almost all down to Eve relinquishing control. It was down to her making a wise call that it was more important for Ted to have fun in that moment than to sleep. Had she tried to force it he'd have resisted, she'd have not been able to (wo)man the stand and it would have been stressful (and she would have had to eat more mince pies as a result.) As it happened, Ted got his play *and* his sleep and Eve got to crack on and help and chat and drink mulled wine, all child-free. Everyone was a winner that day.

Holidays and jet lag

We believe wholeheartedly that if you want to enjoy the early years rather than grit your teeth through much of them, you have to say yes to the opportunities and events that are offered to you. Sleep is important, sure, but so is the sun on your face, salty wind-whipped hair, endless days out, crumbling castle adventures, firefly-finding expeditions *way* after bedtime and spectacular sunset shows. We believe it's always best to just go with it. One of the happiest family holidays Gem ever had was when her gang went to Bali to visit James's sister. Gem was loaded up with all the gear to entertain and pacify her crew on the mega-long flight with three under seven, terrified about them staying awake the whole time, but the boys were magic! They thought it was the best adventure ever. To her complete surprise, they slept beautifully on the flight. Gem on the other hand was worrying about one of them waking and waking the others, so she didn't sleep a wink. Lesson learnt. The entire time they were away, they napped when they were tired, played happily when they weren't, and Gem didn't ever worry about them staying out too late. They just napped the next day. They star-gazed and had some early wakes (thanks, jet lag) so they seized the opportunity to watch the sunrise and they had some lie-ins too. Simply put, they had the time of their lives and sure enough when they returned home, sun-kissed and full to the brim of adventures, they went back to their normal routine and all was well. Nothing was broken. Our advice to you is not to self-sabotage your precious family time away with sleep anxiety or insistence on sticking to strict schedules and routines. We both used to be that person that left the lunch early/ missed out on the play date/scowled at anyone who dared to make a noise during nap time. It's fair to say that exhaustion had us sleep-obsessed. Don't be us! Once self-settling is learnt it can't be broken, only bent a little. Try to remember that your child will always be led by you. If you want them to breeze it, you'll need to too.

Co-sleeping

There is so much conflicting advice out there about co-sleeping. Just typing it in to Google results in an avalanche of information on the topic. Even advice among healthcare professionals can be changeable and conflicting so if you're wondering how on earth you're expected to make an informed, evidence-based decision, it's with good reason.

As mothers, paediatric nurses and sleep supporters, we know first-hand the benefits of co-sleeping. As we've already discovered, we are huge advocates of the fourth trimester and familiar with the reasons why safe co-sleeping can be hugely beneficial for you and for your baby. Research has found that physical contact and close sleeping is known to help babies to regulate their breathing, use their energy more efficiently, experience less environmental stress and encourage better milk supply for breastfed babies in the early weeks and months. Dr James McKenna, PhD, author of *Sleeping with your baby: A parent's guide to co-sleeping* is Professor of Anthropology and the Director of the Mother–Baby Behavioural Sleep Laboratory at the University of Notre Dame. McKenna has researched the benefits of contact sleep and co-sleeping through his work and reports that 'infants and parents sleeping together or in proximity to one another is the way that the nutritional, transportation, social-emotional and thermal needs of human infants continued to be met worldwide.' Babies who are not breastfed also reap the many other benefits of this kind of close contact sleeping. This is because skin-to-skin contact and safe co-sleeping helps us produce that wonderful stuff we spoke about in the fourth trimester called oxytocin. Even mothers who didn't give birth to their babies will still reap the rewards of safe co-sleeping. How amazing is that?

Safe sleep

The spotlight has shone specifically on safe sleep for the last decade or so for good reason. Excluding birth defects, sudden infant death syndrome (SIDS) is the most common cause of death in neonates. In the UK, the Lullaby Trust estimates that around 230 unexplained infant deaths occur each year.[30]

The very reason Gem was so anti co-sleeping before she had her babies was because she saw first-hand the unthinkable when she cared for a family whose baby had died from SIDS when she was a student nurse in London. Gem was utterly heartbroken and will never forget that family and the wound it caused them for as long as she lives. Gem swore she would never co-sleep with any of her babies after witnessing the pain it could cause. When Eve was pregnant with Tilly, Gem remembers calling her on the phone to beg her not to co-sleep. Eve listened but went on to have a wonderful safe co-sleeping experience with each of her four children, based on making the right choices for her own family. And sure enough, when Gem went on to have her own children, and safe co-sleeping was talked about more, she felt much reassured. She was so happy when she discovered that you could keep your baby close and co-sleep in a safe way.

Safe sleep guidance

At the time of print, the Lullaby Trust recommends that if bed sharing is to take place it is made as safe as possible using the following advice:

- △ Keep pillows, sheets, blankets (or any other items that could obstruct their breathing or cause them to overheat) away from your baby. A high proportion of infants who die from SIDS are found with their head covered by loose bedding

- △ Follow all current safe sleep advice such as sleeping the baby on their back

- △ Avoid letting pets or other children in the bed

△ Ensure baby won't fall out of bed or get trapped between the mattress and the wall

We have a duty to tell you that there are some circumstances which the Lullaby Trust says make co-sleeping extremely dangerous:

△ If either you or your partner smokes, even if not inside

△ If either of you have drunk alcohol or taken drugs (including medication that induces drowsiness)

△ If your baby was born before thirty-seven weeks

△ If your baby was born under five and a half pounds

△ Never sleep on a sofa or armchair with your baby. This can increase the risk of SIDS by fifty times

As new research emerges, safe sleep advice is constantly evolving so please do make sure that you keep yourself up to date with the latest advice by checking the Lullaby Trust's website as regularly as you feel necessary. There are so many wonderful 'middle-ground' options now, with next-to-me cribs providing a safe extension of your bed. If you choose to co-sleep (or like Eve find yourself doing so) you are not alone and will never find any judgement here. If co-sleeping ever becomes something that you want to gently move away from, we're your women. Get in touch with us if you'd like some support in how to gently move towards doing sleep a different way.

Your journey, your pace

Through our baby-led approach, we have had the honour of sup-Èporting many families who have wanted to make the changes to their family's sleep at a much slower pace than our typical speedy turnarounds. Kaia's story is one of our favourite 'taking longer' stories.

Kaia's story

They say faith can move mountains, and with a little bit of patience and the assistance of someone like Gemma at C&B, it sure can! I had a bad pregnancy, and a worse postpartum period. Seven months in, I was utterly sleep-deprived and absolutely exhausted physically and emotionally. We had the usual problems: too-frequent night feeds, requiring lengthy presence and frequent pacifier re-plugging to fall asleep at night and movement needed to nap. In general, just too much crying, and not enough *sleeping*.

I knew sleep training would help. I had read the books. I knew it worked. I knew how it worked. I knew the medical community supported it. But most importantly, I knew I was far from the mother and wife I wanted to be – that my daughter and husband deserved. I only had one problem. I couldn't do it. I could not leave my daughter to cry on her own. I wanted the effect of sleep training without actually doing it. A bit of a conundrum, so I reached out to C&B. I spoke to Gemma and explained how my and my daughter's health challenges postpartum had gotten in the way of bonding and fostering attachment the way I had wanted to in the early days. I explained how ultimately, my exhaustion, my fear and my guilt around attachment was distorting my mind, clouding my judgement and stopping me from going ahead with sleep training.

Luckily Gemma was undaunted by my conundrum and foggy mind and took me on. She accepted I needed to do things gradually, gently and in a way that didn't trigger my fear around my daughter feeling abandoned. We focused solely on the next right thing and didn't worry about the end goal. It was a leap of faith.

We started by breaking one sleep association at a time. First removing motion, then the constant pacifier re-plugs. Slowly we increased the delay in my response and moved her cot further away from our bed while I still stayed with her. It was always at my pace and when I felt ready for it. Another big improvement for us came when I realised I had simply been putting her down too soon! And then, one day, what I thought would be impossible, namely leaving the room for her to fall asleep on her own, suddenly felt like the next right thing. There were tears for sure (from both of us), but all the other sleep associations had already been broken, so she accepted it fairly quickly, and it was far easier than I had feared. We were simply both ready. By the time it came to stop night feeding, she barely even put up a protest.

Today, at ten months, she sleeps through the night, she naps in her cot twice a day, and falls asleep fairly quickly and peacefully on her own. I have had a chance to rest, sleep and heal. It was the most important investment I have made in the well-being of my family and it has provided us with more rest than any vacation you could possibly go on with a small child.

As she was so young when we started, we were interrupted by two lengthy periods of teething and developmental leaps where we had to put everything on hold and support her with increased comfort. Afterwards, I was surprised how easily she accepted going back to the pre-teething routine. Now, when there is a period of difficult sleep, I know something is going on with her and I respond to that with patience and increased comfort and support.

I won't say sleep training wasn't hard, but it was not horrific. Gemma's patience, unwavering optimism and stabilising presence guided us through it all. With the incremental progress we made, I was able to process and come to terms with how my fear was what was holding us back, and I leaned in to holding space for my daughter's feelings. I saw that her protest was not a fear of abandonment, but rather frustration that I was changing the habits that I had once taught her, habits that were no longer serving us. She was already ready, I just needed to catch up with her. And in the state that I was in, I could never have done that on my own. So thank you, Gemma and C&B, for enabling me to enable her. Our lives are for ever changed and for ever better for your help.

Room sharing and transitioning

For the first six months of your baby's life, room sharing between adult and baby is not only advised but recommended by the Lullaby Trust. The recommendation is that your baby sleeps in the same room as you for the first six months (and beyond of course if you want to). This is because studies have shown that when babies are close by it can help reduce the risk of SIDS. BASIS (Baby Sleep Info Source) is a project of the Durham University Sleep Centre in the Department of Anthropology at Durham University. BASIS provides practitioners and parents with access to up-to-date, evidence-based research about biologically normal infant sleep with a view to making accurate information accessible to parents and health practitioners. BASIS refer to a number of studies across Europe and in the United States and New Zealand that have shown that babies sleeping in the same room as their parents is associated with fewer SIDS deaths than babies sleeping in a room alone under six months. This does not mean that room sharing protects every baby but the amount by which room sharing reduces SIDS is significant and the Lullaby Trust supports this too.

Each parent is ready to transition their baby to their own room at different times and you won't ever find any judgement here about where on the scale you sit. Eve moved her first baby into her own room at ten months (at the same time that she did the sleep teaching) and her fourth went in at three weeks of age. Neither choice was right or wrong. We support families with sleep and enabling self-settling whether they are room sharing or not. For families who want to en-able self-settling, co-sleeping will need to end so that you're not doing sleep *for* your baby. This can be implemented in the most loving and responsive way possible, whenever you're ready.

To help with the transition from co-sleeping to sleeping in their own room, or sharing with a sibling, our wonderful sleep supporter Lucy (mum of three, including twins, a paediatric nurse and a health visitor) offers some wonderfully clear advice for families facing this change. She advises that when babies are transitioning from multiple night feeds to just one or none, a useful tip is to transition them from their Moses or next-to-me crib to their cot (or the next-to-me crib with the sides on) at the foot of your bed or further away while still in the same room, so you're forging a middle-ground physical separation. This enables close contact and helps parents and babies gradually phase into the transition. The key here is readiness, and whether your babe is pre-six months or post-three years, you can do the transition from co-sleeping to simply room sharing when you're ready. It's a great first port of call.

A common denominator multiple parents share which contributes to their resistance to moving the baby into their own room is an understandable fear of needing to be up and down like a yo-yo to attend to their baby's needs. It's hard enough doing that with your baby in the same room but the thought of having to cross the landing or climb a flight of stairs is enough to put the fear of God into most shattered parents. We always explain that this is a bit of a Catch-22 situation because while you may be attending multiple times to your baby at present, it may well be that the move alone means that you and your baby are disturbing each other less. Not only do you smell of sweet pure heaven to your baby, but the noises you probably don't know you make are likely to be causing some disturbance to them too. We know that when we're exhausted and in that very light, anxious 'hear every murmur' sleep, it's easy to disturb one another with every movement, sigh or grumble (from both of you). Remember that all babies, all *humans*, stir at night, it's how we get *back* to sleep that matters. Doing this transition will limit the chance of you disturbing one another.

Sleep environment

There are no absolute musts when it comes to creating the perfect sleep environment for your baby. This is mainly because there is no such thing as perfect! It can be easy for us to forget that babies have been sleeping since the beginning of time with very few stipulations. Perhaps when you were expecting your baby, you might have had visions of the nursery that they'd sleep in, down to every last detail. Gem spent many a moment of each pregnancy when she allowed her nesting mode to switch into overdrive and conjured up a dream nursery Pinterest board which would rival a Mamas & Papas newly fitted showroom. For many expectant parents, creating a nursery space for your baby is all part of getting ready to welcome them into the world and it can bring great joy. Great marketing and glossy social media pages make it easy for us to forget that we don't *need* all that much. You may want to cover your ears while we say that the world of mass consumption has us believing that we need a series of perfect products, sumptuous soft furnishings and decadent decor to set the perfect sleep scene, when in fact a simple, safe place can be so easily created. All that baby really needs to form their safe haven is you.

When your baby arrives, the reality is that they will spend most of their early weeks and months attached to you, feeding on demand and sleeping any which way that works. The baby's room if you have one often becomes a dumping ground for all the baby gifts (forty-four tiny squares of soft material attached to a small cuddly toy, anyone?!) and other choice household items. There will, of course, come a time when you will go on to use that room when you or your baby are ready to sleep in your own spaces. So there really is no rush. Love, nurture, food and warmth and a few bits of clothing are all your baby really needs. Anything else is a bonus.

You may have heard of the long-held tradition in Finland where expectant mothers are given a cardboard box as part of their government scheme. This concept dates right back to the 1930s. Its aim was to give all children in Finland, no matter what background or home life, an equal start in life. The box contains a baby grow, bath products and nappies, a sleeping bag and bedding. In the bottom of the box there is a small mattress which becomes the baby's first bed. Eighty years on, the box is now an established part of the Finnish beginnings into motherhood, almost like an initiation, uniting generations of women with this one concept. Heikki Väänänen, founder of HappyOrNot, wrote an article that was featured in

Forbes magazine reporting that Finland had been ranked number one in the UN's 2020 world happiness report. It found that Finnish mothers are the happiest in the whole world. Since 2016 some NHS trusts in England now offer baby boxes to parents. We can all learn from the sheer simplicity of this timeless gesture. One little box and four cardboard walls. One big impact.

Darkness

Parents, this section is as important for you as it is for your children! Before the advent of modern technology, we had just two light sources shaping our sleep; the sun and the moon. These natural lights helped us to see during the day, when we were physically and mentally active, and lulled us to sleep at night, when we needed rest. As darkness fell, our brains produced melatonin which lowered blood pressure, glucose levels and body temperature. This helped us to prepare for sleep so that we could rise rested with the sun the next day. Now that we are flooded with artificial light, not just in the form of lamps and lights but the TV, phone and tablet screens which we spend so much of our time on, our sleep is being affected. Melatonin helps us to relax and de-stress and artificial light suppresses it.

But artificial light isn't the only light parents might like to be aware of regarding sleep. Some babies, children and adults will find it very difficult to sleep without total darkness. This is where blackout blinds or curtains can come in handy. Out of Eve's four children, three can sleep in any light and one wakes at 5:00 a.m. if even a glint of light hits his pretty peepers. The bright and birdsong-filled summer mornings can turn sound little sleepers into early risers, and if your child is better suited to a dark room then blackout blinds can help in the summer months to make early wakes a less likely occurrence. There are lots of different variations of blackout blinds you can buy, new or second-hand, and some mobile solutions which are great for summer holidays. It's also really easy to make your own, buying material from a haberdashery (it doesn't fray) and popping it up with some double sided velcro. Eve's homemade ones lasted for years. Like anything that can have an impact on a baby's sleep environment, needs can change, and blackout blinds aren't classed as an 'ing' such as feeding, rocking or anything that does sleep *for* your baby. Babies don't become dependent on environmental factors such as blackout blinds or white noise so use away to your heart's content!

White noise

Whether or not to use white noise causes far more conversation than it needs to. Quite simply, white noise is made up of many different sound frequencies which mask and block out sudden sounds. These may be parents who room share, noisy siblings, knocks at the door, summer birds, enthusiastic delivery drivers and barking dogs, to name but a few. The sound from white noise mimics the sound of the blood rushing through the umbilical cord, so it's a lovely natural sound to use and not something you need to worry about creating a dependency on. We've known of many children who prefer white noise to sleep, but none who can't sleep without it.

It is thought that white noise promotes deeper sleep cycles so is a useful tool for babies who are struggling to link their sleep cycles and who are in a cyclical pattern of light sleep. It's also a great tool to use if you are concerned about another child being woken when you are sleep teaching their sibling. It can be a total lifesaver for when you must share a room with your child when away. One year, Eve's four children (at the time aged one year to six years) slept soundly for three nights in a row just fifty metres from the main stage at Camp Bestival. With the white noise playing in the tent, you could have been anywhere. It meant that the banging tunes and middle of the night toilet stops (those flipping zips!) didn't cause anyone to even stir.

We often get asked how best to implement white noise. Our advice is that it's most effective when played continuously throughout the duration of all sleep rather than it timing out after twenty minutes or a few hours, because this in itself can disturb a baby. We use a device such as a (safe) old phone to play our white noise on and we do this via one of the many free white noise apps. If we use a device we make sure it's on aeroplane mode. The volume should be that of a running shower in the same room as your baby. As a personal preference we prefer pink or brown noise, but choose a sound that feels most calming and peaceful to you; the odds are that your baby will like it too.

Full belly

While we wouldn't be so bold as to tell you how and when to feed your baby, we do think you might find that if you put your baby down to sleep with a full belly, they'll sleep better and longer. Even if a feed isn't due right before your child is due to nap, we recommend that you offer them a top-up prior to it. This way, they can benefit from a warm and full belly before sleep, with no chance of hunger ending a nap prematurely. The whole feeding and sleep topic is contentious, and we are aware that there are lots of differing recommendations with regards to when to feed. Some approaches suggest feeding babies when they wake in order to separate milk from sleep as much as possible. But we don't think it needs to be that extreme.

Our stance on this is that so long as milk is not used to put your baby *to* sleep it is a wonderful tool to come right *before* it. Mother Nature made it so that feeding induces sleepiness, and we want to work with that, not against it. One thing to be sure of is something we have touched on already: try to feed to sleepy but not asleep. If your baby falls asleep while feeding, we advise that you gently rouse them before placing them into their cot, however back to front it feels! Feeding to sleep or feeding back to sleep is the most common obstacle that parents who have sought support from us face. It's the sleep association we have freed parents from in their thousands. Remember, if you're feeding to sleep and it's working for you then great. There is absolutely nothing wrong with feeding your baby to sleep for as long as you want to. There is no such thing as a bad sleep habit. There are only behaviours that go hand in hand with solid sleep and those that don't. All that needs to happen for solid sleep to reign is that a baby knows how to fall asleep feeling sated, loved and safe. That, my friends, is the golden ticket.

Monitor

We know that most parents use a monitor as a safety blanket and take comfort in the fact that they can hear their baby if they need to. What tends to happen, though, is that parents can become reliant on the baby monitor, and, dare we say it, a little bit obsessed with it. We call it *Baby TV*. The downside to a monitor is that you can hear and see every little murmur and movement your child makes, which isn't exactly great for your own solid sleep. Watching your baby (or indeed anyone) sleep might well give the false impression that they are fitful and restless. Take a fitness watch, for example. It can be really worrying to hear how much light sleep you've had, if you didn't know much about sleep cycles. But the truth is that we are all pretty active in our sleep. And we're meant to come in to light sleep very regularly. It's how we are programmed and has no reflection on the quality of deep sleep that we take.

Our advice on monitors is that if you can hear your child crying naturally without the monitor then it might be worth considering turning it off or low. If you can hear your child from where you are, that's a truer picture of their cries or murmurs, rather than an amplified one, and this gives a much more accurate measure of whether or not your baby truly needs you. If you really struggle with letting go of your grip on the monitor, perhaps look at using the video function if you have one, and transitioning yourself to no sound and eventually no monitor, all in your own good time. If you find yourself with a strong resistance to getting rid of the monitor entirely, it could be that there are some underlying issues with letting go. Our resident therapist Felicity is always on hand to help families process and unpick any deep-rooted obstacles linked to sleep and healthy independence.

Sibling/room sharing

Like lots of things on our journey through parenthood, the worry about making the changes is often far worse than the reality. Though of course we understand why this transition can breed anxiety in parents: what if one child wakes the other? How do I manage bedtime? What if one child wakes before the other?

The best advice that we can give on this is to ask you to consider that children have been sharing rooms for centuries. Many without any other option. There can be great joy in siblings room sharing and it can be a wonderful, relaxed experience if you set off on the right foot before you make the move into the same room. It's a good idea to talk to the older sibling about how things are going to be different and to keep some loving boundaries in place with the children room sharing from the start. Staggered bedtimes can help if there is a significant age gap between the children sharing a room, and contrary to popular belief that staggered bedtimes don't work, they often do, especially with white noise. Gem's boys (at the time of writing aged four and seven) go to bed at 6.30 p.m. and 7.30 p.m. Talk to your earlier waker and ask them to come in to you rather than waking their sibling. Stir your children in their sleep as you kiss them goodnight when you go to bed – this can trick the body clock a little and help promote deeper sleep cycles later on in the night, lessening the chance of early wakes. A bowl of porridge or non-sugary snack right before bed (and before teeth) can make as much difference as an extra hour in bed for those who would otherwise wake ravenous. If the worst happens, which sometimes it does, and your children disturb one another, just know that one bad apple doesn't rot the crate. A solution can always be found and all will be well.

Twin sleeping

In the very wise words of our sleep supporter and twin mummy, Lucy, it is extremely rare that one twin will disrupt the other. The common misconception with twin sleeping is that if one twin wakes or disturbs the other that it's going to be catastrophic. Of course, twins can disturb and even wake one another but not always in a way that's going to upset the other twin. Remember that they shared a pretty cosy sleeping space for nine months and are so in tune with one another, finding their own rhythm and how to cope with different levels of disturbance. They have learnt from very early on when they need to pay attention to their twin's noises and when they do not. And more often than not, the disturbed twin will resettle unless they are hungry. In this instance we recommend generally keeping them on the same feeding and sleep schedule which will allow them to be more in sync with sometimes only half an hour difference in schedule. Twins can and do have different sleep needs, they are different people after all. By meeting their needs and enabling self-settling with responsive sleep teaching, life will feel so much more of a breeze and less like double trouble. When sleep teaching twins, most parents opt for some 1:1 support to accompany their plan so that they can talk things through as they go, with someone like Lucy who's walked in their shoes.

We hope this chapter has helped you banish any unwelcome feelings that may have accompanied some of the sleep choices you have made or indeed are yet to make. On a personal note, we long for the day when parents feel entirely liberated in their decisions, confident enough to craft their own approach, armed with the correct and evidence-based info they need to reach that outcome. If our book can go even one step towards helping you do that, we will rest easy.

CHAPTER NINE

PSYCHOLOGICAL OBSTACLES TO SLEEP

When we talk about obstacles to sleep, we might immediately think about physical and health obstacles such as teething, illness, yobbish siblings, the school run, a thunderstorm or the bloody postman who only ever knocks loudly at nap time! These are obstacles of course, most of which we will talk about in the next chapter, but there are often hurdles and barriers of a different kind. These are the obstacles of our hearts and minds – the emotional obstacles to sleep. These can have a significant impact on our ability to enable self-settling in our children, often causing harder-to-overcome disruption until they are identified and understood.

As we walk our path as humans, weaving our way through the great tapestry of life, we will experience hardship and losses of different kinds. Some of us might experience generational or acute trauma and bereavement. Some of us will become parents without our own parents by our side. All these things can contribute to a painful awareness of lack and loss. These things can impact heavily upon how we parent and how we do sleep.

For many people, having a baby can trigger the memory of past experiences, previous loss and significant life events. Some parents may not feel that overwhelming sense of love and connection that they were anticipating. The positive emotions of parenthood are often mixed with feelings of loss, fear, worry, guilt and frustration. One of the toughest things about parenting is that the results of our efforts aren't always obvious or measurable at the time. If we use the immediate behaviour of our children as a measure of how we're doing as parents, there will be days that we're winning, thriving in our parenthood; then there are the other days, ones that have us crushed by the rawness and drowning in the chaos of it all. This is the messy nature of raising beautiful little humans into thriving big ones. Emotional obstacles of many different kinds can come to the forefront of your parenting journey when you least expect it and this can be especially impactful when it comes to sleep.

Our human needs

Maslow's hierarchy of needs is the most widely accepted psychological theory of basic and advanced human needs. Its premise is that the most fundamental human needs, such as achieving one's full potential, self-esteem, belonging, intimacy and creativity cannot be achieved without the most basic needs first being met. Along with food, water and warmth, sleep features at the very foundations of human need. In an article for *SimplyPsychology*, Dr Saul McLeod said, 'Every person is capable and has the desire to move up the hierarchy toward a level of self-actualization. Unfortunately, progress is often disrupted by a failure to meet lower-level needs.'[31]

Maslow's Hierarchy of Need

As you can see, some human needs are universal. But we are also shaped by other factors such as our upbringing, our genetic predisposition, our identity, our personality and our experiences of life. When we talk about sleep and the process of guiding our children to learn the life-skill of self-settling, it can be a multi-layer of different thoughts and feelings. Unpicking these feelings is no mean feat and it can be hard to decipher how we *actually* feel when there is so much 'noise' surrounding what we should and shouldn't do as parents today. This is precisely when we may need to look inward. We each have our own emotional needs; our own set of feelings or conditions that we need to feel happy, fulfilled or at peace. Without them, we may feel frustrated, hurt or dissatisfied. Humans naturally seek emotional nourishment as much as food and water and it is our birth right to be emotionally nourished. If our emotional needs were unmet either as children or as adults, this can have a profound effect on our emotional outlook which in turn impacts how we feel about self-settling. If our emotional outlook has been altered because of past experiences, we may find ourselves with deep-rooted feelings which present as concerns about our child's unmet needs. When parents reflect on their children's needs, they might find that their feelings are more closely linked to their own experiences and fears rather than their child's. In the families we've supported over the years, this has presented in the following ways. Parents may:

- △ Rush in and rescue so as to avoid upset at all costs

- △ Find upset unbearable

- △ Be plagued with guilt about their child's unmet needs

- △ Use disproportionately strong words to describe their child's protest such as abandoned, trauma, neglect and hyperventilation when describing moderate crying

- △ Subconsciously self-sabotage their child's progress (to affirm their child's need for them)

Eve's story

If any of this resonates for you, we want you to know that you are not alone. I once sat on the top step of the stairs and cried my eyes out to Gem over the phone. My eighteen-month-old was waking each night and I, convinced on the surface that it was hunger, begged Gem to help me work out why I couldn't sort his sleep (despite him being my fourth child and this being my job). After an hour on the phone, Gem helped me to dig down to the depths of what was really going on. I discovered that this wasn't about hunger. Or even about Ted. Initially, I was quite cross that she could even suggest that! Why would I voluntarily keep the unnecessary wakes going on purpose?! It really got my back up and was hard to hear. But slowly and gently, Gem helped me to see that I'd been so battered from the broken sleep that I'd been mothering from an emotional distance; drained, snappy, depleted and resentful. In the day, I was pushing my kids away because I had nothing to give them. I was doing the minimum just to get by. I made up for my guilty days with gentle nights. At night, Ted got a different Mummy. I was calm, softly spoken, gentle and nurturing, every sweet stroke of his head a sorry. Sorry for being such a shit mum. Sorry for not being enough. Sorry for being distant. Sorry. It was a total revelation to realise that if I sorted the broken nights, I would be less depleted in the day and not need to make up for anything at night. It was a vicious circle that I had been blind to up to that point. It took my sister to do what I had done for countless families before for me; to help me see clearly what lay beneath and between me and a rested life.

How Gem helped me outlines beautifully how we help families. If Gem had simply told me that Ted didn't need the nightly Weetabix nutritionally, I might have felt guilty and judged. But the way in which she guided me and held space for my feelings gave me the tools to uncover the true obstacle. Myself. This is just how we work as a team; always listening more than we talk, always holding a judgement-free space for parents to bring their obstacles to the surface – known and unknown – where they can be realised and released.

I hope my story helps you to understand that identifying our own deeper obstacles to sleep is not about placing blame or judgement. The journey to solid sleep is highly charged with emotion and complexity and this is where listening ears and open arms are so instrumental to change.

Generational trauma

Generational trauma is something that can crop up out of nowhere. You may have had an incredibly happy childhood and yet still be struggling with certain aspects of parenting, not knowing why it feels so *hard*. The messages we absorb and the stories we are told as children are powerful. Part of the reason for this is that these messages are planted before we know how to challenge and reject them. If you were raised by parents who did not meet your needs, you would understand the injuring scrape of these messages, and their lasting influence on you. The good news is that even if that is your history, you can still find an opportunity to identify and rise above it. To parent in ways that are more open, more informed, more loving and richer than the parenting you received.

You might not have a model of good parenting to guide you, but you know what good parenting feels like to you (even if that's only as a result of what bad parenting felt like). This is when letting your internal compass steer you can be transformational. Parenting takes shape as we go and sometimes the greatest wisdom is contained within experience of trial and error. The greatest parents will be those who are open to those experiences and the lessons they offer. As sleep supporters, there isn't a greater honour than witnessing parents end a legacy of pain and toxicity, empowered with the right tools to give their children, and the generations to come, an opportunity for a new depth of love and nurturing.

Why we parent how we parent

We don't just become a certain type of parent at the click of a finger. There's no mould we step out of, with ready-made opinions and templates about how we're going to parent. However, we'll certainly find ourselves drawn to certain approaches when deciding how we want to raise our children.

How we find ourselves feeding, weaning, potty training and doing sleep is determined in part by our childhood experiences: how it felt to be raised in the way that we were. If our upbringing was largely happy and enabling, we may subconsciously or consciously seek to recreate certain ways our parents did things.

Our mum and dad, for example, were always very relaxed about alcohol as we grew up. From around the age of twelve, we were offered a small amount of some diluted wine with a Sunday roast if we so wished (we always did – the shimmery sherry glasses made us feel *so* grown up) and as a result of alcohol never being prohibited or sensationalised, we never felt much of an urge to drink too much of it as adults. Our parents' relaxed approach to alcohol and drugs (they told us drugs could be really damaging, but did not breathe down our necks about it) meant that we never felt the need to dabble in any of that jazz, either.

It works in reverse, too. If you were raised in a way that didn't work so well for you, you might find yourself choosing to parent in a different way, to create a better experience for your child than the one you had. If you were raised by authoritarian parents at an emotional distance, you may try to balance that out by parenting your own children freely and with less hierarchy. If you felt unseen and unheard, you might make a conscious decision to see and hear your children more. If you didn't experience your parents as understanding, empathetic and emotionally available, you might choose to be more in touch – and on a level – with your own children. You might want to say 'no' less and 'yes' more. You may want to be more their friend than their foe. You may wish to share more with them than your parents shared with you, to forge the connection that perhaps you lacked. This other-end-of-the-scale parenting might be inevitable, but it may also present its own shortfalls, perhaps with the consequence of your own children wanting to tip the balance again when it's their turn to parent. Our own parents were raised sternly, we were raised freely, we are raising our children with more structure and only time will tell how our children will decide to parent. It's an intricately fascinating generational pattern.[32]

All healthy-minded parents want to create the best possible experience for their child, and there is no one formula to do that. As a child, Eve was incessantly praised and largely unchallenged. This resulted in the positives of her having an indomitable confidence and self-belief, but, to consider the other edge of the coin, she found criticism unbearable and boundaries hard to stick to. We have a friend who was parented with strict rules and order. She was supremely organised and resourceful, but found it hard to go off-piste, creatively or physically. Abandoning plans made her feel uneasy and anxious. We helped her learn how wonderful it is to operate off-piste from time to time and sleep reigned.

Our parents came from a generation of disciplinarian parent figures. Our mother was the youngest of six Catholic girls (our grandparents wanted six boys to become six priests!). Having had the honour of speaking to most of our aunts about their childhood, we have found out that while our grandparents were kind and adventurous (Grandma was the Girl Guides captain for years in the Wimbledon area of London) they were at times experienced as emotionally unavailable and inaccessible. We are two of thirteen children born of those six girls, and our cousins and we were all raised with less hierarchy and structure than our mothers were.

The liberally raised children from our family who have gone on to parent have done a bit of a boomerang and decided to install some healthy boundaries and structure in response to the liberal, child-centred upbringing we received. No doubt our own children will tip the balance back again, if they feel they need to. No one parenting approach is a superior one. All have benefits and pit falls. As our dear psychoanalytic aunt Beni once told us: 'However you raise your children, you're going to f*ck them up one way or another!' For all its crassness, this sentiment brought us immense relief because it reaffirmed our belief that all of us are just doing the best we can with the tools we have. We all have different tools. And that's ok. And it's not only ok, it's enough. *It's more than enough.*

Birth after loss

Over the years that we've supported parents around the world with sleep, we've witnessed first-hand how personal loss and trauma can have an impact on how a parent feels about their child's sleep. The absence of a mother's own mother, a traumatic pregnancy or birth, an unforgiving journey to conception or a pregnancy that follows loss can heavily influence how sleep looks and feels. The foreboding agony that follows the loss of a child often takes shape in the form of still-grieving parents who cannot bear the child that follows to endure upset or difficulty.

Like all difficult feelings, grief refuses to dissipate until it has been worked through. Grief will continue to alter the way parents process their and their child's feelings, for sleep cannot escape grief's grasp.

It will act like a pair of grey-tinted glasses, adding meaning where it does not belong (my child feels abandoned) and fear where it is not welcome (what if they don't wake up?). As *Doctor Who* producer Jamie Anderson so poignantly writes:

> Grief, I've learned, is really just love. It's all the love you want to give, but cannot. All that unspent love gathers up in the corners of your eyes, the lump in your throat, and in that hollow part of your chest. Grief is just love with no place to go.

Gem's story

When I had my third miscarriage, I remember having all this love that had grown as my baby did over the three months I carried her. Miscarriage was such an abrupt end and my mother's love had nowhere to go. With my first-born son Toby, who followed two losses, I poured all my lost love into him and felt so lucky to have him that I endured the hard parts of parenting more than I did with the others. I distinctly remember having this overriding feeling of guilt if ever I struggled. Whenever a thought to change anything arose, it was soon replaced and wiped out by guilt.

Previous baby loss can truly impact our journey through parenthood. Zoe Clark-Coates, MBE, is a best-selling author, grief specialist and CEO of the Saying Goodbye charity, part of The Mariposa Trust. Zoe says:

> What I love about Calm & Bright is that they don't minimise parents' concerns and they don't offer a cookie-cutter approach to sleep. They listen, they respond, and in their 1:1 supports they tailor all advice to suit each family's situation. With the right support and peace of mind, restorative sleep is achievable for families who've suffered loss.

Loss lingers. Months and sometimes even years after a beloved new baby arrives, parents can find their joy tinged with sorrow and their excitement punctured with grief. Feelings that may include emptiness, guilt, shame, anxiety and an innate lack of confidence can undermine a parent's perception of how they feel about themselves and their ability to look after their child. This often-subconscious second-guessing can contribute to parents finding it particularly difficult to enable independent settling, because of the distance it creates and the ultimate fear of losing their baby.

Even without a traumatic past, sleep and death have always been inextricably linked. In ancient Greek mythology, sleep was the twin brother of death. The heightened level of vigilance and checking on a baby that follows loss may cause a significant amount of disturbance to the whole household's sleep. If parents appear to act on a level of alert that would suggest it's a matter of life and death, it's because it literally has been. When death has traumatised parents, they will do everything in their power to avoid it happening again. What is the opposite of death? It is a baby who is alive, and is there anything more alive than a wakeful baby?

Parents who have experienced loss tell us that their sleep journey would not have been possible without the nurturing and tender hand-holding that bespoke sleep support provides.

IVF babies

Another clear link that has emerged through our work is between babies who were particularly longed for and disturbed sleep. Parents who've experienced hardship, pain and struggle to get their beautiful baby in their arms in the first place might be less likely to allow them to struggle once they're here. Many IVF parents have had the courage to share with us how having a particularly wanted child can present added pressure to enjoy every moment and embrace the difficulty. As one of our followers commented on an IVF post we shared:

> Thank you so much for bringing this to my awareness. I have experienced this unspeakable guilt if ever I find myself wishing away a sleepless night or a difficult day. It's as if I wanted her

so much, so I better be grateful now she's here. This has made me much less likely to do anything to challenge or change the hard parts.

The thought of allowing your child to experience any upset, when it took so much upset to get them here, can be enough to put many parents who conceived thanks to IVF off sleep teaching in a similar way to parents who've experienced loss. Having an awareness of the root cause of the anxiety around sleep is often enough in itself to liberate parents from it. Working through this with families is what our team is well-equipped to do. Sessions are available with our integrative therapist if the family would like.

Maternal separation anxiety

It is not always just the baby or child who has difficulty separating from the mother. It can also be the other way around. Parental separation anxiety is experienced to differing degrees by a great many parents and it needn't always be a cause for concern. It can develop at any time during pregnancy or the early years and may be brought on by past trauma or mental health struggles following birth.

A mother who experiences separation anxiety from her child is more likely to have a child who suffers from sleep disturbances.[33] A paper published in the *Journal of Child Psychology and Psychiatry* explored the link between maternal anxiety and infact sleep issues and found a strong correlation. The higher the mother's anxiety, the more often an infant woke up at night. This isn't the only research that has found links between a mother's psychological wellbeing and how her child sleeps.[34, 35] A mother who finds separation from her child painful isn't going to be immune from such feelings at night. On the contrary, as we talked about earlier, sleep and the separation it represents can intensify anxiety for parents. While this anxiety presents itself as being about sleep, it often isn't. Sleep is just the conduit for the already existing anxiety to travel through. The anxiety is being experienced *around* sleep but it is *about* separation.

Sabine's story

Sabine is a mother who approached us a few years ago for help with her two-and-a-half-year-old son's sleep. Joseph was taking hours to settle at night and coming into Sabine's bed overnight. No one was getting any sleep.

Thanks to our in-depth assessment, we were able to identify that Sabine was suffering with maternal separation anxiety. She found the nursery drop-off very difficult, worried for Joseph's safety the whole time he was there and regularly called the nursery to check he was ok. She told us that Joseph had separation anxiety and that he struggled to be apart from her. She said he was very clingy when they were together.

We signposted Sabine to some talking therapy to explore her feelings before we worked on sleep. Just a few weeks later when Sabine completed the teaching, she not only had a happy and secure boy who slept all night and settled himself happily within fifteen minutes, she was also able to see that Joseph's problems with separation were in fact more to do with her than him. Joseph found separating hard because Sabine did. As soon as Sabine understood the origins of her feelings around separation, she was able to separate her needs and feelings from his. Sabine and Joseph are two years into solid sleep now and Sabine says that Joseph is more confident than ever.

While it's perfectly normal for parents to experience some degree of worry, anxiety and guilt during short-term separation from their child, if you regularly experience catastrophic thinking, acute fear or overwhelming anxiety, you should access some support from a healthcare professional.

Separation as a trigger

The ultimate goal of sleep teaching is to have a child who sleeps peacefully themselves. But allowing a child to master this already in-built skill might be asking too much of a parent who experiences her child's autonomy as a painful rejection. For many parents, a healthy separation is the ultimate end goal. That is, to raise a child excited about what the world can offer them and what they can offer the world. But for some, separation is unbearable. It is, after all, a form of loss, and it has the power to trigger strong feelings. Where former loss or separation has been experienced in a parent's past, ordinary everyday separations can become problematic and painful. Added meaning from our own experiences can alter how we experience events in our child's life. How we feel about feeding our baby. When we move them into their own room. How soon we give them solids. How we do sleep. How we feel about them starting nursery or being cared for by others. How we feel about a return to work or a much-needed trip away. How we feel about ourselves and how we've processed our life experiences has a significant impact on how we support our children with their behaviour and sleep.

 ## Tori's story

When Tori approached us after over a year of following us on our Instagram page, she told us how she longed for her two-year-old to sleep in his own room. Her husband had been sleeping on the sofa for six months, to allow everyone to get some sleep. But even the things that used to work (bottle, a gentle song) had stopped working and life was a misery. Yet when the sleep issues were solved within a handful of days, Tori felt like she was missing a right arm. We asked her if she would like to get things back as they were, assuring her that she didn't have to make any such changes and she was unequivocal in her answer. She did not want to go back. While she missed her son when he was asleep, she remembered how she'd longed to get even a few hours of uninterrupted sleep before he moved out of her bed. She recognised that her marriage was stronger now that she and her husband were sharing a bed and the difference in her son's happiness and his ability to share and interact with his peers was vastly improved. Missing things as they were does not mean it is healthy or right to return to them.

The 'one person' or loving and letting go

When a parent's identity largely consists of being *the one person* who is able to soothe, feed, nappy change, comfort, medicate and settle their child off to sleep, it can be unsettling to imagine life any other way. When a parent is no longer needed in the way they once were, parents can feel:

△ Regret (should I have done more?)

△ Relief (wait, I get to sleep all night now?)

△ Disbelief (this can't be real)

△ Fear (are they still breathing?)

△ Sadness (so that was the last time they'll ever feed in the night?)

△ Guilt (should I have carried on longer?)

△ Elation (yes, I can go to that hen do now!!!) followed swiftly by all the other emotions above once you arrive!

When a child needs a parent less – when they start to eat, walk, learn, swim, ride, drive, live and love without us always there by their side – parents may ask themselves: what does this mean for my role in my child's world and the way in which I am needed and loved by them?

Whether your baby is six months or sixty years old, they still need and adore you. You are still their soft, safe place. Their ever-flowing well of unconditional love. Their beacon of light when the clouds come over. If your child needs you that little bit less over time, you have simply done the most loving thing of all; you have loved them so hard that they have felt good enough to do it alone. The same deep love that made you hold them close will encourage you to set them free.

Healthy separation

If you love someone, you let them go. Isn't that concept terribly sad at first consideration?! Surely if you love someone you hold them close for ever?! Yet the separateness of self is a key part of the normal emotional and physical development of a human. It begins almost right after birth, with the ritualistic cutting of the umbilical cord, a severance of the physical tie that binds mother and baby. This symbolic step, often carried out by the father, is a celebrated and positive one, marking the baby's ability to survive separately from and outside of the mother. From then on in, each phase brings its own small form of separation. As our babies move from breast to beaker, from bottle to bowl, from lap to chair and from hip to floor, they become naturally able and keen to assert their physical and emotional independence from the mother.

There are four phases in an infant's move towards a separate self.[36] The Emergent Self (birth to two months), the Core Self (two to six months), the Subjective Self (seven to fifteen months) and the Verbal Self after that. As a child forms a sense of their core self, they gain control over their own actions and feelings. A parent who is emotionally and physically available at the beginning of their baby's life builds up a relationship based on connection and trust which gradually helps their baby learn to fend for themself. A parent's reliable presence eventually enables the child to feel safe and secure enough in their connection with their parent, for it to continue even in their absence.

The intense, overpowering intimacy that weaves a mother and her baby together at the start of life naturally gives way to a healthy separation, if the parent allows it. The broad-shouldered eighteen-year-old who drives confidently off in his own car to live the life you did your best to prepare him for, is the same teeny babe who curled his little fingers around yours, mercilessly and entirely dependent on you to meet his every need. The process a mother and her child go through to move from one phase of life to the next involves a great deal of adaption and acceptance of loss and of gain. So, it is perhaps unsurprising that the simple act of putting a baby to sleep, which requires a mother to physically separate from her baby, even if just for a few hours, can be more difficult for some than others. A baby's ability to sleep depends in part on them feeling secure enough to be separate.

Maternal depression

An important variable that seems to have been left out of the conversation about maternal depression is sleep deprivation. One study sought to explore broken sleep as a predictor of maternal depression, taking 505 women who tested low on the Edinburgh Postnatal Depression Scale one week after giving birth. The same women were revisited at four and eight weeks postpartum. The mothers who had 'major depressive symptomatology' were much more likely to report that their baby cried often, woke regularly and that they were getting less than six hours of sleep in a twenty-four-hour period. The results suggested that infant sleep patterns and maternal fatigue are strongly related in the postpartum period. This is hardly surprising. The healing and restorative function of deep sleep helps mothers to process the physiological and emotional wounds of pregnancy and birth. Loss of sleep increases vulnerability and decreases emotional availability, which has a real impact on the mother–infant relationship. In 2009, it was found that maternal depression was the most important psychological factor associated with a child's sleep problems.[37] Mothers with maternal depression might feel disengaged from life (low, tearful, irritable, disinterested, low energy, not good enough, hopeless, guilty) or be in a heightened state of arousal and hyper-vigilance. This can result in more stage-one light sleep, less restorative slow-wave sleep and fragmented REM sleep, which can feed back in to the cycle of depression. But how do we know the difference between postpartum depression and sleep deprivation when they present so similarly?

Common Symptoms of Postpartum Depression and Sleep Deprivation

Symptom	Postpartum Depression	Sleep Deprivation
Irritability	✓	✓
Rage	✓	✓
Emotional volatility	✓	✓
Mood swings	✓	✓
Overwhelm	✓	✓
Guilt	✓	✓
Trouble concentrating	✓	✓
Feelings of low worth	✓	✓
Trouble sleeping even when the baby sleeps	✓	✓
Frequent bouts of crying	✓	✓
Anxiety, fear or panic attack	✓	✓
Loss of interest in things you usually enjoy	✓	✓
Difficulty bonding	✓	✓
Changes to appetite	✓	✓

Jemma's story

I'm writing this as I try on online clothes while both my C&B babies nap. But my sleep story started far less happily. By the time Ivy was six months old, I was on mood stabilisers and my husband had such severe post-natal depression that he was suicidal. I was convinced Ivy had a CMPA but I was being ignored by doctors and was told by the health visitor that I'd be depriving Ivy of nutrients if I cut dairy. (It turns out Ivy was not only allergic to dairy but also to egg.) She was waking hourly at times and on a good night I'd get four straight hours out of her. She never napped – not in the cot, car or pram. Occasionally I'd get forty-five minutes in the carrier (cue a seven kilometre daily walk) but this stopped working at four months. I was getting palpitations and dizziness from the exhaustion but was told by doctors that it was normal for new mums and dads to be tired and find it hard and that the 'colic' would pass. Within one month of buying the plan, we had our lives back. It gave me so much more than sleep – it gave me the confidence to trust my own instincts for the first time ever. A week into her sleeping, I was off the medication. Ivy is now twenty-two months and since we did the plan, she sleeps 6.30 p.m. to 6 a.m., bar the odd illness. She naps for 1.5 to two hours a day. She literally waves us out the door blowing kisses when we put her down and is described as a joy by everyone. She is streaks ahead with her verbal and cognitive skills, which sleep has enabled. I honestly don't know what would have happened with my husband if we hadn't found you. And to think he was reluctant to spend the money!!

Isn't Jemma's story remarkable? How different would her experience have been if she'd have been asked how much sleep she was getting? How different might the start to life be for children and their mothers around the world if all parents were offered support with sleep as a preventative measure for depression?

Feeding and sleeping

To kick off our discussion of the most common sleep obstacles, we're asking the feed-to-sleep association to step up onto stage. At first glance, feeding appears to be a physical rather than a psychological obstacle to sleep. But this isn't ever the case. Because feeding is about hunger it's not a sleep obstacle at all, but a primal need which must be satisfied.

Feeding, whether from breast or bottle, is quite rightly about much more than the satisfaction of hunger. It's about trust and connection. It is about physical and emotional engagement and the dance of attachment. It is about building intimacy, closeness and comfort. All valid human needs. Feeding is one of the first opportunities a parent gets to be responsive. The physical intimacy and closeness that feeding brings is more important to the mother–infant relationship than the source of the nutrition.[38]

But in the sleep-deprived families who approach us, feeding has stopped being about food. Beyond six months of age, feeding in the night can result in additional night wakes because the wake–feed pattern is one you've all become used to. But waking for a feed does not necessarily mean a feed is needed. It may just mean that there is an expectation of one, built from past patterns. It's easy to understand how the association builds. Hunger is a deep and primal concern of a mother. The compelling maternal urge to keep your baby alive through feeding has existed since the beginning of time. How much and how well we feed our baby is ultimately a matter of life and death. How 'well' we do at feeding our baby is also really tied into our sense of worth.

Alongside this primal urge, if you throw in a heavy dose of sleep deprivation, a shot of vulnerability from a difficult birth or worrisome pregnancy, some lingering doubt from a 'failure to thrive' diagnosis and then whisk in some well-meaning but completely conflicting advice from several different sources, it's easy to see how a mother might start to doubt whether her milk (in essence whether *she*) is enough.

This doubt can make it really hard for a tired mum to confidently know that her baby is sated. A great deal of uncertainty about whether they're hungry can be attributed to this. Many breastfeeding mothers interpret any wakefulness in the night as the need for a feed. Because of this, the breast is swiftly presented (hands up, swift breast present-ers – we've got four hands raised here!) and as a result, our babies never get a chance to practise going to sleep without it.

In the first few weeks and months, it is completely normal and necessary for a baby to feed regularly and for them to fall asleep at the breast or bottle. There is absolutely nothing wrong with this. If nature intended feeding and sleeping to be entirely separate it would not have made a mother's breastmilk charged with prolactin –

which, as well as driving milk production, helps to induce sleepiness – and feeding wouldn't trigger oxytocin release, which reduces stress and helps to bond a mother and a baby. So feeding and sleeping are happy partners, but they needn't spoil the fun by getting married! We say that a healthy, well-attached baby of age six months and above can happily go eleven to twelve hours overnight without needing to feed (either by breast or bottle). If additional feeding happens beyond that time frame, or indeed if a baby is fed to sleep either at the beginning of sleep or in the middle of it, then they may come to believe that feeding is the only way they can fall asleep. If every time a baby or child wakes they are fed, they might very well come to expect it at every wake, which, as we know from looking at the structure of sleep cycles earlier, is very often.

When feeding becomes the only way that a child knows how to sleep, it can feel a desperate situation for the parents. Being the only person who has the tools to do sleep is as much a burden as it is an honour.

Parents may find that babies and children who are feeding more than they need to are much more likely to be less interested in food. It is a bit of a catch 22 situation. Parents feed their eight month old through the night because they're not interested in solids during the day. And then they're not hungry enough in the day. So they feed them at night. This might materialise in a mother who says her baby isn't interested in breakfast, yet has offered it to him just an hour after his first feed, when he's not yet hungry. Swapping a feed for food first (with the feed following later, before the nap) can make a huge difference. Another reason a baby may have a slower uptake to solids is if the mother subconsciously sees her baby/child as younger than they are. Mothers can almost be surprised to say their child's age in years instead of months! When mothers who reach out to us describe their almost three-year-old in months (thirty-three months) this can indicate that she might be holding on to the concept of her child as a baby, rather than the young child that they are. Accepting that they are older might mean facing the fact that the baby phase is over. This can raise difficult feelings about the mother's role as her little one transitions from baby to child. Accepting a child's actual age can shine a spotlight on areas that might benefit from change – change that the mother may not be ready for. When a child's age is given in months beyond two-and-a-half years old, we always take care to consider whether the mother is quite ready to make changes and what support she might need in place to be able to do so.

Parents who rely on breastfeeding as the only way to do sleep often approach us feeling quite hopeless. They find it almost impossible to imagine that sleep is possible without the magic of the breast. The association with bottle-fed babies can be just as strong except that this can feel less desperate because someone else is usually able to offer the feed. The thing to remember is this: if a baby is put to sleep either through feeding or rocking or staying, they are not *getting* themselves to sleep, we are *putting* them to sleep. We are doing sleep for them. We cannot expect our children to have the tools to do sleep themselves if we do not give them the opportunity to practise it. It is not that our children *can't* sleep without feeding, it is that they don't yet *know* how. But that's ok, because that's precisely what you can teach them via a plan designed to enable self-settling. While we could talk until the cows come home about feeding in relation to sleep, we are by no means lactation consultants. If you need any support regarding breastfeeding, please seek out an International Board Certification Lactation Consultant (IBCLC) who will be able to answer any questions you may have.

Emotional factors

We ask families to think about what is on their emotional horizon before they consider starting any sleep teaching. By that, we mean any life events that will have an impact on the emotional welfare of either the child or the parents. These include a house move, the arrival of a new baby, a return to work or a start in a new childcare setting. We recommend that parents avoid starting any sleep teaching too close to such an event so that the child does not connect the new way of doing sleep with any other change. A toddler who is forked out of his cot and bedroom just a week before the shiny new baby arrives might feel justifiably usurped. Time and space is needed for him to process this huge change to the world as he knows it before any other changes are made.

When a mother returns to work it is often a time of emotional conflict. The fleeting excitement and adrenaline at the prospect of doing something outside of the home is often marred by the deep-running dread about how things will be done when you're not there to do them as only you know how. Gem and I have experienced intense feelings of guilt. Guilt associated with an emotional change such as the ones mentioned above can often be the root cause of a sleep regression. We feel guilty about our return to work so (perhaps despite our children feeling fine about it) we make up for it at bedtime and overnight by allowing behaviours to pass or creep in that we'd not previously allowed.

How parents interfere with sleep

The settling to sleep process is a natural, biological adaptation that, if not interfered with, usually happens by the age of four to five months.[39] A peaceful settle to sleep involves a baby being put into their cot sleepy but awake (and we like nice, full tummies, too) allowing them to peacefully drift off to sleep themselves . Babies are born with the ability to link their sleep cycles and if we as parents can find the confidence to hold off and not rush in once we feel they're ready, we can let the magic happen and the natural course of things take hold.

The more 'secure' an attachment style the mother has (low levels of anxiety), the more able she will feel to find other ways to put her child to sleep, passing on her confidence to the infant, enabling him to develop his independent sleep skills with his inherited confidence.

One of the loudest cries of the anti-controlled-crying movement is that we must respond to our babies when they cry. And we couldn't agree more. What's of key importance is that we respond *appropriately* to those cries. Sometimes that is absolutely picking them up and feeding them. But it is certainly not always. Parents have a larger part to play in their baby's sleep than they might think; they can either support their baby to do what nature intended and allow them to do what they are perfectly capable of, or they can introduce well-meaning sleep habits and associations that can become ingrained and hard to break free from later on.

Parent-introduced fears

Most parents are surprised to discover that some of the fears we think our children have are in fact parent-introduced concepts. No child is born afraid of the dark, for example. The most protective, secure and life-sustaining haven – where every one of us spends the first nine months of life – is as dark as dark can be. A 'fear' of the dark can be created at the click of the finger, with a simple, innocuous parental suggestion that a light is left on. Perhaps the parent was once afraid of the dark themselves and knew it felt better for them with it on. When parents suggest a light, we do it to reassure. But it also suggests to them that there might be scary things they can't see without the light.

Another great example of a parent-introduced concept is the cot to bed transition.

Picture this, you decide it's time for your two-year-old to move into a big bed. You have a new baby on the way who will be using the cot, and your child is now able to get out of the cot himself so it is no longer safe. You excitedly set the scene for the change, per-haps sourcing new bedding for the big bed, talking to your toddler about the change now that he's a big boy, perhaps even changing the room round to signal the next chapter of sleep! It's all going swimmingly until . . . you innocently do something that most parents do. You make it clear to him that just because he *can* get out of bed doesn't mean he *should*. You go further, giving more detail! 'Remember, you must stay in bed, darling. Don't come into Mummy and Daddy's room overnight. Stay in your bed until morning, ok?' Unbeknownst to you, you just made the likelihood of him getting out of bed and breaking your – and his – sleep far greater. Having slept in a place where he's never been able to get out, it hasn't even occurred to him that he could – or should – ever get out. Your well-meaning pep talk, though, has introduced this as a new and exciting possibility! And so, what might have been his first peaceful and triumphant night of sleeping in a big bed without so much as a peep, ends up with him taking you up on your suggestion at an ungodly hour! This shows how easily a 'fear' or a belief can be introduced.

The cot

Some parents are convinced that their baby hates the cot and views it as a prison. The 'bars' association is an adult one, though, not a baby or child's, and there is no reason for a healthy, well-attached child to develop a genuine fear or phobia of the place in which they sleep under normal circumstances. They may fear their sleep cues being misunderstood, or resist being put to sleep in a place they have not become used to settling in, but that is more of a resistance to – than a fear of – the cot. Parents who come to us concerned that their baby or child has a fear of the cot are often reluctant to embrace any sleep teaching because of it. We find that apparent 'cot fear' or aversion is ruled out once self-settling is enabled.

 Claire's Story

Fourteen-month-old called Toby slept beautifully night and day until he hit thirteen months. Despite still settling himself peacefully to sleep at night, naps had become a real problem. He had begun refusing to go down for his second nap. He began to cling to his mum when she was walking him up the stairs for his second sleep, as if he was scared, and Claire was convinced that he had developed a fear of his cot.

We explained to Claire how between nine to fifteen months a baby is usually gearing up for the transition to one nap, which actually takes place around the ages of fifteen to eighteen months. Toby was taking such a big morning nap (one and a half hours) that he wasn't tired enough to go down for his second nap. His clinging to Mum was about him saying that he wasn't ready for sleep. Once Mum knew about the nap transition and we advised her to cap the morning nap at forty-five minutes so that he was tired enough for his second nap, he went back to willingly and happily entering his cot at nap time, rolling over to one side and drifting peacefully off to sleep within a few minutes. Toby's perceived fear of the cot had just been about him asking his mum to give his nap timings a little jiggle.

Pain

Pain is another sleep obstacle that brings much confusion and ambiguity. While real pain does of course interrupt sound sleep (we will look at this in detail in the next chapter), parents who have historically avoided sleep teaching because they've been convinced their child is in pain are often surprised to hear that the concept of pain can be something they themselves can introduce. It is very easily done. When a child restlessly thrashes their legs about for example, it is natural and responsible for a parent to ask their child if they are in pain. This is a genuine, well-meant question, but it is a leading one. The child, wanting and needing a reason and a label for their discomfort, and knowing that pain equates to some attention and love if everyone's shattered and ratty, might well say yes. In this case, the 'pain' is actually an unwillingness to settle themselves back off to sleep for whatever reason, and the restlessness and frustration that this brings may well masquerade as pain. Pain then becomes the accepted reason for the broken sleep by both parent and child. The longer this goes on, the more life and strength it gains, and it snowballs and gains a life of its own. One mum had accepted her daughter's leg pain for two years as the reason she didn't sleep. Three hours into the sleep support, Mum saw it for what it was – her daughter's way of seeking some much-needed attention, which, when sleep was enabled and Mum wasn't so tired, she was able to give freely in the day time. This eliminated the need for it at night.

Many families give pain relief routinely before sleep, even if it doesn't make a difference to the perceived 'pain' or the quality of the child's sleep. This in itself can become a learned behaviour. Many a child has learned to wake for a quick comforting medicine administration, however banal a pay-off for waking it seems.

If ever pain is in question, parents may find it helpful to ask their child what they're feeling, rather than if they're in pain.

Helen's Story

Helen had had to fend for herself from a very young age. She had often felt afraid and alone. She approached us as a mother of two young girls aged four and six, and pregnant with her third child. Helen was convinced that the girls could not sleep because they were scared. They had their own room, but getting them to sleep took an age unless Helen or her husband lay with them, and even once they were asleep, they'd never stay in their own beds. Every night, Helen's family of four was co-sleeping, and the girls 'windmilled' through the night. The thought of adding a newborn baby into the mix prompted her to seek our help. The girls had been complaining of growing pains, restless legs, sore backs and being afraid of monsters for a very long time.

Understandably, her daughters' fears froze Helen into inaction, allowing the broken sleep to go on and on. It was a vicious cycle that went on for over a year.

When we began working with Helen, we helped her to think about which fears belonged to her and her past and which were more likely her children's. Then we let our method do the talking.

Helen was in a state of shock when, forty-five minutes into our responsive sleep teaching on the first night, the girls went from being apparently upset (while we regularly and lovingly attended to them) to making dinosaur noises, giggling and snorting. An hour in, they were in hysterics, and Helen and I were both laughing with them. Helen's exact words were 'well, that doesn't sound like two terrified little girls to me!' The spell had been broken!

It was truly beautiful to watch Helen arrive naturally at her own conclusion that none of the fear she thought her girls had been experiencing was real. Her childhood fears, which had arisen – with good intention – to protect her beloveds from feeling the way she'd once felt, got put back in their rightful place, and she was able within a few days to watch the girls peacefully settle off to sleep each night in their own beds and wake happily eleven to twelve hours later. Helen enjoyed three months of solid sleep and the energy her body needed to prepare for the birth of her baby. She never looked back.

Breaking the cycle of generational trauma

We are not able to change the experiences we had as a child, but we can seek to understand them. We certainly have the power to change how our past experiences affect how we live and parent. A painful childhood does not have to mean patterns are repeated when we become parents ourselves. On the contrary, gaining consciousness about how we were impacted gives us an opportunity to have a fresh start. In fact, every day brings a new chance for parents who were not raised as they deserved to be to understand and unpick the injuring scrape of the messages they received about themselves as a child. The lasting legacy of a harmful parental influence really can be another generation of parents who choose to love their children as they themselves deserved to be loved. To give their children what they never had. This is no easy task – it is one that requires the parent to look inward and do some hard work where it's needed. When a hurt child parents, there is a beautiful opportunity for them to parent in ways that are more open, more love-led, more compassionate and richer for the wisdom and insight that has been fuelled by their history. We've seen and experienced it ourselves. Love can overcome.

We can highly recommend Dr Nicole Le Pera's book *How to Do the Work* as a powerful navigation tool if you want to dive into your past pain so that you can turn it into something beautiful in the future.

Jacinder's Story

Thanks to our in-depth Family Information Form that we use to ask parents about their physical and psychological history, we discovered Jacinder's heart-breaking story. Jacinder was locked in a garage as a young teen by her caregiver and regularly left to cry until she fell silent. This could go on for hours on end. Unsurprisingly, Jacinder found it triggering to hear her baby upset for even a moment. She felt she had no choice but to rush in, scoop her baby up in her arms and make everything ok. She comforted her baby with the same strength of love that her inner child had missed. The result was multiple night wakings and Jacinder being on high alert at all times, night and day. So even when her baby did sleep, she could not. She and her baby were exhausted. But this wasn't only about us rushing in or a straightforward plan. It was imperative that we supported Jacinder to give voice to her trauma so that she could separate her feelings from her baby's. It was an honour to be able to witness her untangle her trauma from her daughter's sleep teaching so that she could stop the generational trauma continuing its destructive course. The result was beautiful: a released and rested mother and a joyful, sparkle-in-the-eye baby. Jacinder was back in touch recently, some years after her sleep support, to tell us that sleep had enabled her to have the headspace to do some proper trauma work which had freed her further.

If you stuck around for this somewhat hard-going chapter, thank you for bearing with us as we shared what we felt we must. We have tried to tread the fine and delicate line by sharing what parents need to know, without adding blame to already tired and vulnerable parents. As you can see, the work we do is about so much more than sleep.

CHAPTER TEN

PHYSICAL HEALTH OBSTACLES TO SLEEP

No baby or child (or adult for that matter) can be expected to sleep their best sleep when they're not feeling 100 per cent themselves. Illness and pain, both mild and chronic, can have a huge impact on sleep, and the main culprits might not be what you think. Did you know, for example, that most parents find the common cold poses more of a threat to sleep than a tummy bug?! (This is particularly so if your little one uses a dummy because their blocked nose makes it impossible to suck on one. While we're on the topic, that's a really great opportunity to get rid of the dummy!)

It can be very hard for parents to know how much of their child's poor sleep is down to illness or pain. And therefore, whether and when to work on sleep or wait until the illness or discomfort passes. Some parents battle on for months (and sometimes years) with poor sleep, blaming it on the latest regression/teething/leap/illness/whatever they can find on Google. While all these factors can have a fleeting impact on sleep, there is a longer-lasting impact of such hurdles too. When parents doubt whether their little ones are 100 per cent well, they intervene a lot more with their child's sleep, which leaves the child with less opportunity to do the thing they're totally capable of; sleeping soundly alone. A parent's confidence in letting their child do sleep themselves is undermined when they're uncertain about whether they're 100 per cent. This often sees them revert to old ways of soothing a child, which can become ingrained over a long period of time. Especially if the comfort isn't needed. Of course, when there really is something going on, your child will need extra help and support from you with sleep. We're going to help you understand the most common physical health obstacles families face. And then we'll show you how to overcome them. Shall we get started?

SOS

When your family is struck by a health obstacle it's *hard work,* whether good sleep is your norm or not. If you have become used to a full night's sleep and then have the solid sleep rug whipped from under your feet, you can actually feel more tired than if you are living on broken sleep long term. If you've been living on less sleep than you need for some time (greater than a few months) you will have acclimatised to it. Your lower energy, worse mood, reduced concentration and impaired strength of body and mind will have become your new norm, and you will have lowered your expectations on what sleep should look like to meet where you're at. You will have forgotten how it felt to be rested. Countless parents are sleepwalking through their life, unaware that they're operating in a significantly impaired state.

If your family once suffered from sleep deprivation before making solid sleep your new norm, you might find sleep setbacks especially frightening. When sleep temporarily reverts due to a health obstacle or a change to the sleep environment (such as having to stay in the same room as your child while away from home) you may find that you're gripped by an overwhelming fear that your all-important sleep is going out the window. You may find yourself catastrophising with thoughts like:

△ We've gone back to square one!

△ All our hard work is undone!

△ What's the point of even staying away if it ruins sleep?

△ We're never going to sleep again!

While this might seem overly dramatic to a non-tired parent, trust us when we say that these feelings are real. If you've felt these feelings, it's because you will remember the toxicity of exhaustion as if it were yesterday, and you'll do anything it takes to avoid ever going back there. You fear that you won't cope if the sleep you enabled is taken away. This is all completely understandable. But hear us when we tell you that while your worries are understandable, they have been magnified by your fear of the *what if*s. The hurdle becomes more of a threat to sleep when you add the layer of your panic or anxiety about what it means long term. You might also find that you've become obsessed with getting sleep *right*, so that you never return to when it felt so *wrong*. This is a sign that there is still some anxiety woven around sleep from your sleep-deprived days. It can be a sign that you'd benefit from talking through your fears with a counsellor who has a good knowledge of sleep-related anxiety (such as our in-house therapist). Deciding to talk to someone about your anxiety surrounding sleep helps not only you to understand your feelings but it also prevents your child from picking up on the fact that sleep is stressful and angst filled.

While we know it's easier said than done, try not to get ahead of yourself when the threat to sleep hits. Even becoming conscious that you're catastrophising will help. Know that whenever there's a hurdle, there's no way that sleep will go back to how it was, unless you go back to doing what you did before (all of the time, for a considerable amount of time!). Solid sleep is like riding a bike – a child never forgets, so long as their parents don't put the stabilisers back on!

If you've never had solid sleep, a passing health hurdle such as a sickness bug is a serious threat to the already thin ice you've all been skating on. Eve remembers being frozen by fear if ever she heard there was a sickness bug about. She catastrophised the hell out of life, often spending days gripped with fear (and counting down the days until her children were clear from being in contact with the sick kid). Nowadays, with solid sleep the norm, it's not such a big deal. While the washing is a bit of a ball ache, and no one likes sick, a few nights of broken sleep is no catastrophe when you know you can catch up on sleep in a few short days. It's when there's no light at the end of the tunnel and no chance for reprieve, no chance to catch up on the lost sleep, that the panic sets in. What's the answer if solid nights are your exception and not the rule? Change it, my love.

The ladder of comfort

In our plans we refer to something called the ladder of comfort. We use this 'ladder' to explain to parents the process of increasing levels of comfort.

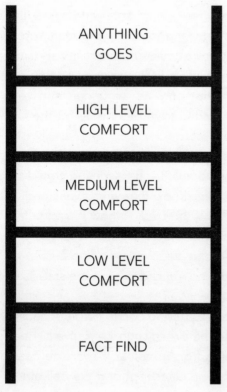

ANYTHING GOES

If none of the other steps are working, do whatever it takes to comfort them. This may be feeding or rocking or co-sleeping.

HIGH LEVEL COMFORT

Stay and comfort your child in their cot/bed until they are asleep.

MEDIUM LEVEL COMFORT

Offer comfort more frequently through gentle touch and words, not picking up. Stay longer and leave once settled.

LOW LEVEL COMFORT

Give adequate pain relief and offer a little more comfort than usual. Presume they're ok unless they show you otherwise.

FACT FIND

What's the problem? Is it affecting feeding or sleeping? If NO, continue as usual. If YES, go up a step.

If a child is faced with a physical obstacle to their sleep – teething or a cold, for instance – we would start at the bottom of the ladder. The first thing we ask parents to do is to consider whether the obstacle is impacting their feeding or sleeping. If it isn't, no matter how worried you might be about what *could be*, we urge you to carry on as normal with what *is*. Presume the best and prepare for the worst by giving your little one the benefit of the doubt and having what you might need to hand such as Calpol and a snot sucker! If your child gives you reason to believe that they are struggling with sleep, give them a little comfort and some adequate pain relief and see if that does the job. Presume at this point that they're going to be ok and that they don't need more from you at this point. Trust that your child will let you know if they're not ok. If they show you that they're not really ok, at all, don't hesitate to go straight up to the next rung of the ladder – the next level of comfort. Medium-level support involves offering a little more comfort more frequently through gentle touch and words and staying a little longer until your baby is settled. If when you leave the room your baby hasn't settled off to sleep then go up the ladder to the high level of comfort. As you can see from our ladder of comfort diagram, at the very top of the ladder is 'Anything goes'. This means that if none of the other steps are working, do whatever it takes to comfort your baby. This may mean feeding or rocking or co-sleeping. There is absolutely nothing wrong with this and it will not get you into a pickle in the future, so long as you walk back down the ladder with confidence once your child is feeling better.

Our ladder of comfort encourages parents to not rush in at the top of the ladder with things like co-sleeping, rocking and feeding them to sleep the minute we suspect they're a bit under the weather. Instead, we advise starting at the foot of the ladder and going up one rung at a time, not hesitating to up the comfort when needed. While it might be unavoidable, do *try* not to go back to any sleep association that you've worked hard to overcome (unless of course the illness requires that extra fluids are needed, in which case, feed away!). Experiment with other ways to comfort at first. Reverting to the sleep association that used to be their *one thing* can take a bit of work to move back away from.

We frequently get asked by parents if it's ok to go back to increased comfort responses when babies are unwell, and our response is always the same. It's actually really important *not* to hold back on the comfort for fear of breaking the good sleep if it is genuinely needed. You're more likely to disrupt the good sleep by attempting to 'stick to your guns' and enable self-settling in a poorly child who needs some comfort. This is asking too much of them. Parents are often surprised when we talk about safe co-sleeping with our children when they're poorly. Offering a drink through the night. Extra love and cuddles on tap. This is exactly what we recommend doing when our babies aren't 100 per cent. Our approach is about being a responsive parent, it's about tuning in to your baby's needs and knowing that it's ok (and important) that your responses change when they need to. All is not lost when you have to take a few steps back. You'll soon be leaping forward again.

Common childhood health obstacles

Teething

Teething is probably the most common health obstacle that has most parents second-guessing whether their children are in pain or if they are ok. Teething typically starts around six months when the first teeth (deciduous or milk teeth) emerge through the gums, but signs of teething can start as early as three months according to the British Dental Association. Some babies' teeth emerge with no pain or discomfort at all, while others will have symptoms such as sore and red gums, flushed cheeks, excessive dribbling, the need to chew on things, and maybe going off their food and being slightly more fractious than usual. Teething can often go hand in hand with an upset tummy due to the excess saliva pooling at the pit of the stomach which causes diarrhoea and a sore bottom.

Most children have all their milk teeth by the time they are three years old. Of the seven children we have between us, some haven't batted an eyelid when it comes to teething, while others have had mild to severe symptoms causing broken nights and some gruelling days. So, it's important that we reiterate again that all children respond differently to teething. This is why it's so important to tune in to our babies and what they're telling us. We have gotten through buckets of Calpol over the last twelve years. Teeth tend to come through in pairs, but there are some children who cut a gazillion teeth hard and fast, which can cause more significant problems in relation to sleep. Gem's Louis was one of those babies; he had a full set of teeth by the time he was twenty-two months old, which was *heaps* of fun!

This is where the ladder of comfort that we just talked about can come in useful. We begin by assuming our babies are ok – giving pain relief and starting with the usual level of comfort – and then increasing comfort and reassurance as we need to.

It can feel like your baby is teething for the whole first three years of their life but in reality, they are not. Each episode of teething shouldn't last longer than a handful of days, unless they're cutting multiple teeth. A good indicator to help you unpick this is how your children appear in themselves in between sleep. Are they showing some of the signs we mentioned above but seem ok? Are they off their food? Irritable? Or do you sense it's bothering them? Your gut is your best tool to work this out.

It is common for parents to use teething as a go-to excuse every time a baby is irritable or sleep is broken. We've all done it subconsciously at some point. It can help if we stay mindful that teething will only continue for a short time with each teething episode and there's absolutely no reason why you can't have some glorious sleep in between teething episodes. If your little one has been teething for what seems like for ever, ask yourself if it's really teeth, or whether you're at a bit of a loss as to what it is. A label such as teething can give bewildered parents a semblance of control and a clear reason for the wakes. If this resonates with you, it might be worth trying to find out what else could be beneath the night wakings. Could it be that *the ings* have taken hold? Have a think about whether remedying those wakes once and for all is something that would benefit your family.

Common cold and viruses

The impact of the common cold on your little one's sleep has been massively underestimated. For starters, the ears, nose and throat are so closely linked that congestion and discomfort on any level can cause havoc with your baby's senses. Think how 'off' you can feel with a cold. Our babies are no different. As mentioned earlier, congestion can be particularly problematic when it comes to infant feeding and the use of dummies because a blocked nose can make sucking impossible, which can be distressing for both parent and child.

If your child is out of sorts and you're worried, then of course you may need to increase your comfort responses and nurse them to good health. This might mean all the cuddles and lots of the good stuff, such as a multivitamin and a probiotic, which can help boost immunity for pre-schoolers who seem to come home from nursery and pre-school with a bit more than you bargained for (a nice cold or flu virus to accompany the copious amounts of painted pictures and junk modelling!).

Gem always recommends Vicks VapoRub on their feet at night, which contains a powerful blend of ingredients such as camphor, menthol, eucalyptus, cedar leaf oil, nutmeg oil, thymol and turpentine oil. Pop some socks over the top to lock the goodness in. Children's paracetamol and ibuprofen can help reduce symptoms of a sore throat and sore ears. (Please follow guidelines on the packet.) While rare, common colds can lead to more serious health implications, such as viral induced wheeze, chest infections and other respiratory illnesses like croup and bronchiolitis. We recommend always consulting your healthcare provider if you're worried about your child.

Sickness bugs

Sickness bugs are the devil incarnate, aren't they? There's nothing like that feeling of dread when your child comes into your room at 3 a.m. saying, 'Mummy, I feel sick.' That's if they're considerate enough to give you any warning. That split-second feeling of doom is as if a chime rings, signalling your demise! Just writing about it gives us the heebie jeebies. Sometimes, of course, those fears are realised and the whole family can be taken down like dominos. We can laugh about it now but many a time we've had our children playing vomiting tag team. And with multiple children, it can take a couple of weeks or more for it to work its way through the family. It's really fun stuff, especially when it times itself so that your child can't go to the one event they've been looking forward to, such as Eve's dear Ted's fourth birthday party. The bouncy castle was up, the party bags made, food all ready and with one hour to go he chundered, meaning the whole party was cancelled. Joy.

Over the years we've learnt to flap less when our child is being sick. We make sure we are just there, rubbing a back if needed and talking calmly and confidently to cover the shitting-ourselves feelings that we have. 'You're ok, my lovely, I'm right here. You're doing so well. Nearly done.'

A good practical bit of advice is something we called the layered sheet trick. This is useful during sickness bugs but also when potty training at night. Set down a layer of disposable change mats (or towels with a bin liner underneath) and then a sheet on top. Create another layer and repeat with up to three layers. If the sheets need changing in the night you can rip off a layer and have a ready-made bed underneath! This saves you from the delightful challenge of finding sheets and making beds at an ungodly hour.

During the sickness bug, increase fluids and feed little and often. Make sure they're getting a sugary drink such as juice or squash in them if they're not eating anything. Eve once had her three-year-old admitted to hospital to receive intravenous fluids after she continued giving her daughter water and not juice, thinking it was healthier!! Call on all the help you can get (laundrettes are very useful when the whole family comes down with a ghastly bug).

Increase levels of comfort and do what you need to do to all get some sleep. Let your child eat when they want to. But start small and dry such as dry cereal or dry toast. Once your child is better, which is usually sooner than you think, and often long before you've recovered yourself, a probiotic is a good idea for building up that healthy gut bacteria. Pesky bugs, be gone! Sickness should usually stop within one to two days. Seek immediate medical advice by calling 111 if your child:

△ Has any signs of dehydration such as weeing less than normal or dark/smelly wee after using (or refusing) dehydration sachets

△ Stops feeding while they're ill

△ Keeps being sick and can't keep fluids down

△ Sickness hasn't stopped within two days

△ You're worried about them

Reflux
Reflux is another health obstacle that has a direct and indirect impact on sleep. Not only does it present its own physical obstacles, but the increased comfort and upright position and contact sleeping it often requires can mean that sleep is disturbed long after the reflux has passed. Reflux impacts both feeding and sleep. When your baby is born, whether you are breast or bottle feeding, there's nothing like the togetherness and intimacy that comes from feeding your baby. But for some babies, reflux can throw in a serious curveball.

Mild reflux is common in babies and may just be a sign that they've had enough food. The oesophagus (food pipe) is shorter and narrower in babies than in older children and adults, and the muscular valve at the bottom of the oesophagus, which stops milk feeds from reflexing back up, is also underdeveloped. In addition to this, our adult food pipes and stomachs, and the lining of both, are able to tolerate and withstand acid. Babies don't yet have this function and these factors can cause pain, discomfort and vomiting. Common childhood reflux usually gets better on its own, but sometimes it doesn't! If your baby's symptoms of reflux continue past two weeks of time (note: not two weeks of age) it is recommended to seek advice from your GP or healthcare practitioner.

SYMPTOMS OF REFLUX

△ Being sick or positing during or shortly after feeding

△ Coughing or hiccupping when feeding

△ Swallowing or gulping after feeding

△ Back arching

△ Inconsolable crying/colic, usually in the evening (more gripe/wind pain than normal)

△ Refusing a feed

△ Not gaining weight

△ Broken sleep

△ Constipation

△ Diarrhoea

△ Funky-smelling breath (caused by ketones from vomiting)

△ In more serious cases of reflux, blood in vomit and poo (very rare)

Silent reflux

When babies are vomiting/posseting, reflux is reasonably easily to diagnose, but there are some babies who may have the signs of reflux but who don't vomit, and this is known as silent reflux. It is much harder to diagnose silent reflux in babies.

SYMPTOMS OF SILENT REFLUX

△ Chronic coughing

△ Gagging

△ Choking

△ Nasal congestion

△ Pauses in breathing (apnoea)

△ Cyanosis (blue around the lips)

△ Noisy breathing including wheeze and hoarseness

The early months are hard enough for new parents. Adding reflux or silent reflux on to the parenting table adds a whole new level of difficulty. Navigating through any of these obstacles can be incredibly hard, not least because so many parents struggle to get a diagnosis. Even once the diagnosis arrives, parents often feel unsupported on their journey, having their unique experiences dismissed as normal and something their baby will grow out of. While this may be true, there are other times that it is not. Some babies will need medicating. Others will have an intolerance or allergy beneath the reflux. These parents need listening ears, practical support and emotional hand-holding. When parents reach out to us feeling confused, conflicted and unheard, we will always encourage them to confidently advocate for their child and to continue to seek the support and guidance that they need even if that means an uphill battle. You are the expert in your baby. If your gut tells you something is wrong you must listen to it. Reach out to a healthcare professional if you would like some help or support with your baby's reflux.

HOW TO HELP YOUR BABY WITH REFLUX

According to the World Health Organisation and UNICEF, breastmilk is better digested than formula milk and contains enzymes that aid digestion, so the chances of reflux in breastfed babies is slightly reduced. If you are formula-feeding your baby, then there are some good reflux-friendly formulas available including lactose and/or dairy-free formulas which can be a more suitable option for babies with reflux. For some babies, thickened expressed breast milk and formula can ease reflux symptoms. Seek medical advice from a dietician or health visitor to see if this is a suitable option for your baby. In bottle-fed babies, feeding little and often and more slowly can be hugely beneficial, as can burping your baby frequently and keeping baby upright for half an hour after feeding. In some cases, very rarely, surgery might be needed to strengthen the muscles to stop the food or milk from travelling back up. This will be advised if necessary, by your child and family healthcare team.

Gem learnt about many things that can help reflux in babies in her five years spent nursing babies with reflux and CMPA in London on a gastroenterology unit for children. In this time, she became aware of some of the many fantastic natural remedies out there to help ease symptoms of reflux, including organic gripe water and remedies such as Calmosine (genius stuff) and a jolly good non-dairy probiotic such as the Biocare non-dairy one. How wonderful that after many years of only prescribing generic medicines for reflux we are now looking at the bigger holistic picture, to make good news of the remedies that mother nature can offer us. We recommend doing your research on this. There is so much out there to help and soothe your baby.

SLEEP AND REFLUX

Reflux is a hurdle to solid sleep, but it is totally overcomeable! Gem and Lucy, who are our in-house paediatric nurses, have extensive experience in supporting families with sleep when babies have reflux. It is so rewarding to support a family as they get the kind of sleep they so long for and deserve, having experienced all the challenges that come with having a baby that has reflux. So, for all of you reflux mummies out there – keep the faith and don't lose hope. Things can and will be better. We are here to listen to and support you.

Colic

Isn't colic a bit of a minefield? Babies with colic are defined as those who cry a lot for no obvious reason. Colicky babies are otherwise well (and not hungry) yet cry for long periods of time. Colic can start a few weeks after birth and usually peaks between four and six weeks of age. Babies usually grow out of it by the time they are three to four months old. Yet for parents who live it, it can seem like years rather than months. Hours spent with your baby inconsolably crying while you walk around the room or resort to taking them out in the car at 3 a.m. just so the crying will stop. Praying for it to stop. Colic is an endurance test for any parent. It presents in babies who:

- △ Cry inconsolably for three or more hours regularly when not hungry
- △ Are hard to soothe or comfort
- △ Have clenched fists
- △ Go red in the face
- △ Are particularly windy/uncomfortable at their core
- △ Bring their knees up to their tummy

Here are some things that you might find helpful:

- △ Anti-colic drops or medication
- △ Calmosine and Biocare non-dairy probiotic (you can take these yourself if you're breastfeeding or add to your baby's milk if not)
- △ Keeping a food diary if you're a breastfeeding mother (some mothers believe dairy exacerbates their baby's colic)
- △ Cranial osteopathy
- △ Increased contact such as baby wearing and safe co-sleeping
- △ Keeping your baby upright after a feed
- △ Thorough winding (there are some great YouTube videos out there)
- △ Warm lavender baths
- △ Rocking and motion
- △ White noise

There are some childcare professionals who specialise in colic if you feel your case is particularly severe. Do get in touch with us if you'd like us to signpost you.

Constipation

There's is no such thing as 'normal' when it comes to how often a baby should poo. From six weeks of age, breastfed babies can sometimes go for several days or even a week without having a poo, without being constipated. As you get to know your baby you will quickly get used to their poo habits, so you'll be able to tell what is normal for them and what isn't. Constipation makes it more difficult for your baby to have a poo.

SYMPTOMS OF CONSTIPATION

- △ Pooing fewer than three times a week
- △ Straining and finding it difficult to poo
- △ Dry, hard lumpy or pellet-like poos
- △ Unusually smelly wind and poos
- △ Refusing feeds or being more fussy than usual
- △ Small amounts of bleeding if the poo tears the anus as it comes out

For babies, constipation can be caused by a change in your diet (if you're breastfeeding) or a change in infant formula. Constipation can also happen when weaning your baby onto solids foods as their digestive system adjusts to the new demands on it. If it passes quickly, it's nothing to worry about – just their body learning how to cope with digesting the new foods. Constipation can also be triggered by a lack of fluids. This is typical when babies are teething, meaning they're not drinking what they usually would. Needless to say, this is usually remedied when they become well again and are able to eat and drink normally. In older children, it can be physical or psychological. White carbs can block them up – think white bread, crackers, wraps. And it can also be emotional, as Eve experienced first-hand.

REMEDIES

△ Ensure you're eating enough fibre if you're breastfeeding (apples, pears and prunes are particularly good for constipation, give them to your child to eat if they're on solids)

△ Bicycle massage (when your baby is lying down, take their ankles and move their legs in a cycling motion to get the bowel moving)

△ Baby massage

△ A warm bath

△ A good probiotic such as Biocare non-dairy

Constipation can disturb sleep short term. If it is a long-term condition, it can increase anxiety and a fear of being alone (incase a painful poo will come and the parent won't be there). The tummy is such a focal area of both physical and emotional difficulty that when there is discomfort of any sort, it can, of course, cause excessive wakes and worry. Don't hesitate to give more comfort and do all you can to alleviate your child's symptoms, but be confident enough to know you can scale it back when the constipation clears. For chronic or persistent constipation, homeopathy can be wonderful. Eve has had huge success with homeopathy curing her six-year-old daughter's chronic constipation which lasted for two years, despite being on the same diet as the other three children and despite seeing several very expensive health specialists! In Sena's case, it turned out that she was 'holding on' to some emotional stuff, and this was mimicked in her subconscious 'holding on' to her stools. It was something she could control. After one course of homeopathic remedy (which Sena loved so much she reminded Eve to give them to her three times a day!) she was clear and free of it and has never suffered from that day. It's been two years now. A good homeopath will want to talk to you and ask you lots of questions before prescribing the right remedy. Eve paid around £30 for diagnosis and treatment combined.

Allergies and intolerances

We are seeing an increased number of babies and children who are presenting with a confirmed diagnosis of cows' milk protein allergy (CMPA) or showing signs and symptoms of having a cows' milk lactose intolerance. CMPA and lactose intolerance are not the same thing, but they are often confused with each other because they are caused by the same factor (cows' milk). The difference is that CMPA involves the immune system and lactose intolerance does not. So while lots of the symptoms are the same, children with an allergy to cows' milk protein can have more profound symptoms of allergies – such as an itchy rash, wheezing, runny noses and coughs. These can also be seen in lactose intolerance, but may not be as obvious, making this condition often harder to diagnose. With lactose intolerance the digestive system can't fully digest lactose (the sugar found in milk). So instead of being digested and absorbed, the lactose stays in the gut and causes the symptoms of lactose intolerance, which can be built up over time.

SHARED SYMPTOMS OF CMPA AND LACTOSE INTOLERANCE

△ Painful wind

△ Colic (defined as excessive crying or fussiness)

△ Bloated tummy

△ Diarrhoea

△ Tummy aches and cramps

△ Wind at the bottom end

△ Nausea and vomiting

△ Congestion and a constant runny nose

△ Eczema – mild or severe

△ Redness and dryness of the skin

△ Refusing feeds

CMPA-SPECIFIC SYMPTOMS

△ Allergy symptoms (as above but more can be more severe)

△ In severe cases, anaphylaxis

△ Blood in stools

Lots of babies will present with CMPA and lactose intolerance in the early weeks and months and then go on to grow out of them. Over the last decade we've noticed a positive change in the support that is offered to families who have children with allergies. We are hopeful that the same support and acknowledgement will evolve for babies with intolerances too. We're forever growing and learning about these things. Sometimes, you may have to push for an assessment. Push away if your gut tells you that something is up. You are probably right.

When thinking about CMPA and lactose intolerance it's important to consider how much discomfort your child might be in. In this instance of course we would recommend increasing levels of comfort until or while proper investigations are underway. Consider that most babies with tummy troubles have different, ever-changing needs, including how frequently they feed and the position that they need to be in post-feed.

There are other common and less common allergies in children. We have focused mainly on CMPA and CMPI in relation to feeding and sleeping but there are of course other childhood allergies that can have an impact on sleep. Speak to your GP or healthcare practitioner if you're worried about allergies or intolerances in your child.

Sleep disturbance

It's not uncommon for parents to be more wary about enabling self-settling if their child has suffered from reflux as a small baby, or had a run of illness. But as we discussed above, sleep disturbances that continue after colic has been resolved are often down to the fact that the baby became used to being kept upright and in close after a feed.

We have supported lots of parents who didn't reach out to access support because they felt they'd 'built a rod for their own back' by offering increased comfort and responsiveness because of their child's reflux or other tummy/health problems. We always reassure them that they did absolutely nothing wrong by offering increased comfort to their babies when they needed it the most. On the contrary, it's because they did it right. We assure them that we'd have recommended the same had we advised them at the time. We tell them without judgement that meeting their baby's needs in that very moment was exactly what they needed to do and is precisely the reason why, now that their babies are better, they are able to learn how to self-settle with the right support and guidance.

Other physical obstacles to sleep

Here are some other physical and environmental factors that can have an impact on sleep.

A dirty nappy

In the early days and weeks, meconium-filled nappies and frequent poos through the night are common, and a dirty nappy is obviously going to disturb your child's sleep. As you come out of the fourth trimester, your baby's bowel habits will be more consistent, and it will become much more common for them to poo in the daytime.

If your baby's nappies are leaking from wee, it might be worth looking at changing nappy brands or sizing up. Nowadays nappies are very absorbent and the right one for your baby will last them for twelve hours. If yours isn't, go up a size, check it's fastened properly, change nappy brand or think about what time of day your baby is having their fluids. For toddlers and children who are needing a wee in the night or waking with a sodden nappy, consider cutting back on fluids after teatime. Milk is not needed as a drink beyond twelve months, although it can of course still be given. The nutrients that milk provides – calcium and protein – can be readily given in other sources. If your child is older than twelve months and you'd like to consider getting rid of the bottle but still keep a pre-bedtime milk drink in place, try giving it to them further away from bedtime in a suitable cup (there are some brilliant non-spill ones on the market). Above the age of twelve months, always brush your little one's teeth after milk and before sleep.

ROOM TEMPERATURE

Your baby being too hot or too cold can have an impact on safety as well as sleep. The chance of SIDS is higher in babies who get too hot. The safest temperature for your baby or child to sleep in is 16 to 20 degrees Celsius with light bedding or a sleep sack. In summer, keep windows open or use a fan to regulate the room temperature. Breastfeeding mothers may wish to breastfeed more than normal in hot weather to ensure their child has enough fluids. Bottle-feeding mothers can offer a baby cooled boiled water between feeds. A good tip to tell how warm or cold your baby is, is to touch the nape of their neck. Note: their hands and feet will always be cooler. If your baby's skin feels too hot or sweaty, remove a layer of clothes or bedding. When your baby is unwell they need fewer, not more, bedclothes. This will give you a good indicator of their body temperature alongside the room thermometer if you have one, though we never have. Changing the sleepwear and sleeping bag/quilt tog based on the season should help too.

Sleep and illness

After your baby has been unwell, you're likely to want to get sleep back on track at the first opportunity, not least because of sleep's healing properties. As your child returns to full health they will be able (and want) to get back to full rest. While some parents can't wait to get back on track, others may use their child's illness as a green light to revert to heightened physical and emotional closeness, long beyond when they need it. While there isn't anything wrong with this per se (a parent has the right to give as much comfort as they wish), it may be helpful for parents to recognise and separate their own needs from their child's. Eve's poem at the back of the book might help you to do this.

Know that most babies aren't able to return to normal sleep until a good five or so days after they first appear back to full health. So go easy on them. Even if your child has a chronic health need that makes it hard for parents to identify whether the sleep problems are related to the condition (in which case, make allowances) or are just self-settling issues. In our experience there is no chronic condition that doesn't benefit from the healing properties of better sleep. With a thorough assessment from our paediatric nurse team, families who face health obstacles can access honest, judgement-free support and communication. It is in this manner that sleep really can be transformed. Your child is never beyond help and there is always hope!

Hope for better days

Remember that each baby and child will respond differently to illness and teething. Some children will have quite a high tolerance to it and not bat an eyelid, while others will be more impacted. Just like us adults with varying immunity and pain tolerance. This takes us back to acknowledging that you are the expert in your child, and you will come to know how they handle these obstacles – and what their norm is – so that you can respond accordingly to meet their needs. Keeping your confidence is key. When life throws hurdles your way that disrupt sleep and you are challenged, remember that peaceful, restorative sleep never need be too far away. It is you who will confidently lead your child back to the rest they need and are capable of.

It's also important to acknowledge that while we might worry about how awful sleep will be when our children are unwell, our children aren't looking so far ahead. Gem's experience as a children's nurse over the last eighteen years has taught her that all children respond to health obstacles and trauma in their own way. How the adult handles it also impacts the child, of course. On the paediatric cardiac ward where Gem worked, where children were routinely having open heart surgery, they'd be walking around the ward with drains and tubes attached the very next day, full of the joys of spring and ready for solid sleep that night. When children feel bad, they tell us. When they feel better, they tell us too. We need only to tune in to that. Be guided by your child's pace of recovery.

CHAPTER ELEVEN

TROUBLESHOOTING

In this chapter, we are going to troubleshoot the sleep struggles that cause parents the most headaches. Before we get into this though, we are going to cover some super simple C&B basics, so that we are all singing off the same hymn sheet! Here we go.

C&B basics

Nap gaps (not nap times)

Let's start by saying that you need to throw out your clock. Ok, we're not *actually* asking you to do this, as that would be silly. But we are asking you to consider using it in an entirely different way. Because never will you hear us telling you to put your baby to sleep at a certain time. Wait, what?! There's no routine to stick to? No. There is not one time specified in our plans.

Once, we were contacted by a parent who demanded a refund the moment she opened our plan and realised that it didn't tell her exactly when to do what. She said she'd come seeking sleep and how on earth was she meant to get it if she didn't have a fixed routine? The glowing review she sent us five days later revealed how gobsmacked she was that her seventeen-month-old had gone from taking two hours to settle down for each sleep to settling 'like magic' within five minutes every single time. He went from waking three times a night to smashing out twelve hours a night within six days! This mother explained how she hadn't realised how freeing it was to be able to carve out her own routine using the tools provided. She'd always thought sleep only came alongside a rigid routine. Needless to say, she no longer wanted the refund!

This mum wasn't alone in telling us how liberating she found it to be given a tool belt to craft her child's sleep, rather than a rulebook to bash herself with. Parents who come to us having used other approaches with more rigid times to adhere to, tell us in their hordes that when they 'fail' to meet the times stipulated they feel like a failure. Trying to remedy broken sleep while not being able to follow the time frames creates feelings of inadequacy, of not measuring up and of feeling incapable of sticking to plan. That *they're* the problem, not the impossible to follow plan.

We don't know how a time can be stuck to when 'real life' variables are added in, as they so often are with child sleep, especially when there are other siblings to work around. For example, if your six-month-old usually has a 9 a.m. nap, but wakes at 6 a.m. or 8 a.m. instead of their usual 7 a.m. – or has a really broken night – how will it work for them to still go down at 9 a.m. regardless? What if that baby's ready for bed hours before their nap time? Way before they're *supposed* to be? Do you just ignore what they're telling you and showing you and starve them of sleep or put them down when they're not tired? Of course not. Your baby's sleep is ever evolving and so must your approach to it be. Being adaptable and letting go of the need to control their sleep will result in you feeling much more in control, because you are never going to get sleep 'wrong'. You want to feel like you're swimming with the tide and not against it. Instead of trying to fit your baby's sleep patterns into a neat little box, we offer you permission to quit clock watching and take up baby watching instead. It works wonders.

To work off nap *gaps* rather than nap *times*, and what your baby is *showing you they need* rather than what they are *supposed to be doing,* might just be the most stress-reducing decision you make as a parent. After all, your little person will only ever march to the beat of their own drum, not yours. Resistance is futile!

WHAT IS A NAP GAP?

To start with, let's be clear on the lingo, shall we? A nap gap is the amount of time your baby is *awake between sleeps* during the day. Due to a whole host of conflicting information and popular but poor advice, most parents who approach us are keeping their babies up *way* too long for their age. Families are often gobsmacked to discover how little time their baby is able to be happily awake. They're relieved when they hear how simple the answer is which explains their baby's fussing, general mardiness, nightmare naps and endless sleep battles. Being told they're just a bit too tired to sleep is such a relief to parents. Its simplicity helps parents feel they can fix this! Discovering how much day sleep your little one can take and still go through the night can be a real revelation. It won't take long for you to realise that the good night sleep that follows good day sleep is not *despite* the great naps, but *because* of them. It takes an unlearning of previous rules or approaches to allow the new good, far simpler stuff to sink in and take hold.

Understanding the nap gap has a brilliant ripple effect. Whether your little one is three weeks or three years old, sussing what amount of awake time works best for them will positively impact on pretty much every area. Expect everything to be better: their mood, the length of the nap, how peacefully and quickly they settle to sleep and the night sleep too. It will also improve your confidence in your own ability to read your child's sleep cues and meet their needs. This has a knock-on effect of making you feel like you *get* your child and are nailing this parent lark.

The smallest nap gap starts with the youngest age, as outlined in our Sleep Needs Table. At one month old, a baby's nap gap is a minuscule forty-five minutes. This means that forty-five minutes after your baby wakes from their last sleep, they'll most likely want to be asleep again. Anything that needs to come before sleep, like a nappy change, a feed or a wind, needs to take place within that time. We are quite aware that this might feel like a pathetic amount of time to play with. That's mainly because it is. But try to think of it this way – every forty-five minutes you get a little bit of a break, even for twenty minutes. When your little one sleeps you may get an opportunity to rest (always top of list), wash (mainly last), put your feet up (100 per cent down for that), batch cook, have an uninterrupted shower or poo, avidly clean (not ever on Eve's agenda) or spend time bonding with another child if this isn't your first rodeo. It's up to you whether you view the cup as half full or half empty and this can be a conscious decision you make daily. (Tip: solid sleep helps it feel full to the brim.)

The nap gap increases by around fifteen minutes each month in the first year of life. So, at two months of age we work off a baseline of a one hour nap gap, at three months one and a quarter hours, at four months one and a half hours and at six months around two hours.

Understand your child's sleep needs

The parents we help tell us that our Sleep Needs Table is super snazzy. And who are we to disagree?! The table is there to give you a baseline to work from. Once you understand the basics for a typical child's sleep and feeding requirements at each age, you'll have the confidence to go off-piste and find your own rhythm that works for you. The table provides you with a typical child's sleep needs, night and day, from birth through to age six. It will tell you the nap gaps, (time awake during the day between sleeps), the number of naps needed, when they drop a nap and the average total day sleep and number of overnight feeds needed. Parents have described the table as 'an absolute godsend', 'a real eye-opener' and a 'game-changer' when it comes to understanding sleep. Which pleases us greatly! We hope you find it at least one of these things.

Our table is there to serve and guide you, not to tell you what to do and when. It matters not if your baby sleeps outside of our base-line guide. What matters is that you and your baby get the sleep you need. You'll know whether your little one is getting enough shut-eye by observing how happy they are between sleeps.

Sleep Needs Table – Newborn–18 Months

Age (Months)	Awake Period	Day Sleep (Hrs)	Naps	Night Sleep (Hrs)	Night Feeds
1	45 mins	6–8	6–7	8–12	on demand
2	1 hr	5–7	5–6	9–12	on demand
3	1 hr 15 mins	4.5–5.5	4–5	11–12	2–3
4	1 hr 30 mins	4–5	4	11–12	1–2
5	1 hr 45 mins	4–5	3	11–12	up to 1
6	2 hrs	4	3	11–12	0
7	2 hrs 15 mins	3.5–4.5	2–3	11–12	0
8	2 hrs 30 mins	3.5–4.5	2	11–12	0
9	2 hrs 45 mins	3–4	2	11–12	0
10	3 hrs	2.5–3.5	2	11–12	0
11	3 hrs 15 mins	2.5–3.5	2	11–12	0
12	3 hrs 30 mins	2.5–3.5	2	11–12	0
18	4 - 5 hrs	1.5–3	1	11–12	0

Sleep Needs Table – 1.5–6 Years

Age (Years)	Awake Period	Day Sleep (Hrs)	Naps	Night Sleep (Hrs)	Night Feeds
1.5	4–5 hrs	1.5–3	1	11–12	0
2	4.5–5 hrs	1–2.5	1	11–12	0
3	5–6 hrs	0–1.5	0–1	11–12	0
4	12 hrs	0	0	11–12	0
5	12 hrs	0	0	11–12	0
6	12 hrs	0	0	11–12	0

SIGNS YOUR BABY IS GETTING ENOUGH REST

Your baby:

- △ Is largely happy between sleeps
- △ Looks rested and refreshed (no dark under eyes, rosy cheeks)
- △ Is emotionally secure, confident and well-attached
- △ Wakes from day and night sleep happy most of the time
- △ Falls peacefully asleep within five to fifteen minutes on the whole
- △ Sleeps pretty solidly overnight 95 per cent of the time
- △ Wakes at a reasonable time of day (for us, this is 6 a.m. onwards)

If you feel sleep is working for you and your baby, you might not feel the need to reference our table. (If it ain't broke, don't fix it!) You may choose to feed your baby more regularly than our table suggests. This is of course ok too. It's your baby and your choice. So long as it is safe and in their best interests, you have our blessing to do sleep whichever way you like. Our table outlines the number of feeds a healthy, thriving baby needs, but if you've been advised by a qualified health professional to feed your baby more than we suggest during the night because they are low weight or failing to thrive (or if you just want to) please do. Bear in mind that giving surplus feeds in addition to what a baby needs can encourage more night wakes than are necessary. Parents who choose to feed more than their baby needs may find that they reach a point where they need to decide what they want to encourage more: the additional feeding or the additional sleeping. There is no right answer to this question.

SIGNS YOUR BABY MIGHT NOT BE GETTING ENOUGH REST

Your baby:

△ Feels or looks shattered

△ Can't happily last their awake time

△ Constantly rubs their eyes or yawns

△ Battles sleep

△ Takes too-short naps (thirty minutes or less)

△ Wakes from sleep crying

△ Is constantly clingy or insecure or hard work

△ Refuses naps or bedtime

△ Wakes in the night beyond six months

△ Wakes before 6 a.m. most days

△ Is being routinely woken from day sleep

USING THE SLEEP GUIDE

Our Sleep Needs Table recommendations are based on babies and children who are getting a full night's sleep (of eleven to twelve solid hours) and taking lovely long, restorative naps. Needless to say, most parents encounter the Sleep Needs Table when sleep looks very different from this. If your baby is already on a sleep deficit, you will almost certainly need to shorten the times provided. After a broken night or an early start, feel free to ignore the gap and pop them down as soon as they're tired. Either let them sleep as long as they want to or wake them up after forty-five minutes to encourage the next sleep to be longer. You'll need to experiment and use your intuition to decide which one will work best for you that particular day. We call an earlier than usual sleep a catch-up nap but it's less of a nap and more of an extension of the lost overnight sleep. A catch-up nap can sometimes be enough to reset the day sleep, getting you back on track. Except for cat naps (third naps that happen up to the age of seven or so months of age and usually last between twenty and forty-five minutes), restorative naps usually last between forty-five minutes to two and a half hours.

INTUITION

Further to remembering that the table is very much a *guide* rather than a data-driven formula, we ask you to use it alongside an enhanced awareness of your child's particular sleep cues. Don't let anything we (or anyone else) says about sleep override your intuition. The nap gap is fluid and can change on a day-to-day basis. If your six-month-old baby, whose usual nap gap is two hours, had a really crappy night, they may well be ready to go back to sleep again less than an hour after waking up. If they're absolutely hanging – their sleepy little head practically in their porridge – don't stretch them because the Sleep Needs Table says they should be awake for another two hours. If they're tired, put them down. If they've had enough sleep, get them up!

On the other end of the scale, be prepared to lengthen the nap gap between the last nap and bed (some find the last gap before bed to be an hour longer than the nap gap.) Or stretch it if they take longer than fifteen minutes to drop off, by getting them up and trying again later. If your baby drops naps or hits other milestones earlier than their peers, they may need larger nap gaps and earlier nap transitions. Tune in to what they are showing you they need. Getting naps right is all about trial and error, using the Sleep Needs Table as your reference point.

OVERTIREDNESS

Ultimately, when your child is tired, let them sleep. Sounds simple, right? But with all the conflicting advice out there, there's a huge amount of confusion over when to put a baby or toddler down for a sleep. Parents can understandably feel like they're being asked the impossible when they're told not to let their babies get overtired (often resulting in anxious parents putting a child down way before they are sleepy enough) while at the same time being told to make sure they tire them out! While physical exertion, daylight, fresh air and a bit of social interaction are always a good thing, babies don't need to be *tired out* to sleep. Being a brand-new human developing at lightning speed is taxing enough! During the first three years of life, a child makes more than one million neural connections per second. That's enough to do them in. Overtiredness is not something to be afraid of or anxious about, but it's definitely something to be aware of. Babies don't need to be exhausted to sleep. In fact, it's much less likely they will sleep if they are. When a wake window is missed, your little one gets an injection of adrenaline and cortisol pumped into their bloodstream, making it:

△ Harder for them to settle

△ More likely to have shorter naps

△ More likely that poor day sleep will mean a poor night

It can be hard to make the call that your child is overtired because they often appear full of beans, wide awake and wired. But a baby who seems not tired enough to sleep is often *too* tired. It's just as important not to become obsessed with avoiding overtiredness. If we swing to the other end of the pendulum, we can put them down before they're ready which can result in lengthier settles and an unhappy baby and parent. Sleep teaching where sleep teaching is not needed. When you're trying different nap gaps, try to be open to what your baby is showing you they want and need. If your child wakes happy from a nap, they've probably had enough sleep for now. If they don't, they may be too tired and need to go down sooner next time.

Don't rush in
You might find it helpful not to rush in when your baby wakes from a sleep, be that a nap, an early morning wake-up call or during the

night. Many parents using the C&B approach have noticed that when they find the confidence to hold off, their little ones are actually very content to wake up slowly and naturally after a nap, often cooing or babbling happily to themselves for up to half an hour before they want to be picked up. We used to leave our little ones in their cot to come around in their own time if they'd woken up happy which was almost always, as they were getting the rest they needed. It was so lovely to hear them happily coming to, as peaceful as could be. Not only did it give us that extra bit of time before jumping back into all-consuming mother duties, it meant that each day they were confidently building their skills up to manage varying stages of sleep alone. Clever clogs!

We often tell parents to hold off at night too. Instead of following our urge to rush in and rescue, to intervene and speed up the process, we encourage parents to hold back, allowing them the opportunity to work it out for themselves. This can feel counter-intuitive and frustrating at first. Why would we hold off and make our life harder by allowing them to wake fully up and keeping the whole house awake longer, when we knew a quick feed, pat or rock would do the trick? But we soon learnt that investing a little extra time initially meant that they had the opportunity they needed to practise the skills they were perfectly capable of putting into place. Which shortened/eliminated the wakes over time. We had been taking the easier option, but it wasn't really easier over time, it was just easier in the moment. Choosing the least easy option in the moment meant better sleep long-term. Allowing your baby that time to work it out (always intervening if frustration turns to upset) gives them the opportunity to build on those crucial independent settling skills. The return on investment is well worth the effort. If you can allow yourself to give them these small opportunities too, you'll soon have a baby who is super content in their own company, safe in the knowledge that their needs are met. We think you'll find it a total pleasure to peek in and watch them in that wonderful post-sleep state where all that is required of them is to just be. It will also mean that they might take themselves back off to sleep after a natural rouse. This can be a real revelation too! Going in to get them when they first wake can actually interrupt their sleep, shortening the nap that would have lasted a lot longer had you found the confidence to hold off a little and witness the wonder of them doing their own thing.

Conscious feeding

It took Eve until her third baby to develop her sanity-saving *feed last* motto. With her first two babes Eve had breastfed them when they were hot, cold, happy, sad, afraid and bored. (Oh and when they were hungry!) The big guns (breastages) had been administered at all times night and day without much thought as to whether they were actually required. Eve's gung-ho approach resulted in a hell of a lot of shite sleep, and sore nips, so the third time around Eve was determined to find another way to do sleep. What was the point of mistakes if she didn't learn from them!

Conscious feeding can still go hand in hand with feeding on demand. It's simply about feeding objectively, it's about thinking about whether your baby is in fact calling for a feed or something else instead. It doesn't mean you don't feed a hungry baby, of course, it just means that you momentarily shift out of zombified auto-pilot and think about it first for a second or two. If your baby signals they want to feed but had a whopper of a feed only forty minutes ago, you might like to ask yourself if it could be anything else. Could they be seeking comfort for a sore bottom, or might they be a bit uncomfortable? Could they want a change of scenery or be overstimulated? Could they be trying to tell you that they're too hot or too cold? Could they be tired and just wanting to sleep? Once you've taken a minute or so to do these speedy mental checks, you might deduce that tiredness is at play. More often than not, it is. If so, you might like to try popping them down for a nap after a lovely feed. If you've ruled the rest out and hunger is at play, feed away!

Cluster Feeding

Don't be alarmed if your breastfed baby wants to cluster feed late into the evening. A lot of babies want to be held close and to feed constantly from early evening until very late (11ish seemed to be our little ones' bedtime for the first few months of life). If a baby needs to cluster feed to build up their breast milk supply with the aim of having a longer stretch at night, this is completely normal and nothing to worry about. If you'd like to rule out hunger as the cause for endless cluster feeding, you might want to give a bottle of expressed breast or formula milk which will very quickly tell you if hunger is what's at play. Both of us had babies who cluster fed way into the tenth week of life. Some of our children were supplemented with formula. Some weren't. It did not have an impact on how long they went on to breastfeed for.

For Eve, the reason for the cluster feeding was that her supply was less enthusiastic at the end of a long day, especially as she had three other little people under age six to care for. The best advice Eve had to up her supply (from our dear mum) was to replace every other feed with a glass of water. We were also both advised to stock up on the natural herb fenugreek, known to boost milk supplies. For breastfeeding advice and support, we recommend finding one of the many kind-hearted, open-minded, non-judgemental lactation consultants out there who will make you feel supported and empowered and make sure your breastfeeding journey lasts as long as you want it to. Don't for one moment think that you have to pick between breast feeding and sleep teaching. We've lost count of the times someone has attributed their extended breastfeeding to sleep teaching (because proper rest had taken the place of resentment).

Introducing a bottle
If you are breastfeeding and want to introduce a bottle for mixed feeding purposes (as Eve says, this was her best feeding experience out of all four children) we recommend that you think about introducing a bottle by the three-to-four-week mark, once breastfeeding is established. If you leave it too long, it is possible that your baby might refuse the bottle. We found breastfeeding most enjoyable and flexible when it was accompanied with the last feed of the day being done by our partners before they went to bed,

which was always later than us anyway. This meant that if we went to bed early ourselves after the last feed around 7/8 p.m., and our partners gave the 10 p.m. feed, we were getting a glorious six solid hours of sleep at the beginning of our night from very early on. This was a complete, total and utter game-changer.

Fed is best

While we are touching on feeding, we think it's a perfectly wonderful time to tell you that *fed* is best. This comes from two breastfeeding mums. Do not give anyone permission to guilt-trip you into believing that you are a bad mother if you can't, or don't want to, breastfeed. That includes anyone who offers you an opinion that makes you feel bad; the 'well-meaning' mother-in-law, the friend or a mummy group member and even that outspoken, passive-aggressive social media keyboard warrior.

Eve's Story

I'm ashamed to say that I was only one step away from being one of those anti-formula feeding people at one point. I didn't know it at the time, but I was super smug about how easy I found breastfeeding my first two babes and how much milk I naturally produced. I thought, because of my own experience, that everyone would find it this natural if they only tried hard enough. (I know, I know. I'm cringing too!) If, like me, you were lucky enough to find breastfeeding a doddle, try to remember that that's not everyone's experience. Before you look judgementally at a bottle-feeding mother across the way from you, consider that a woman may not be able to breastfeed for a whole host of reasons including:

- ▲ A medical condition or illness requiring radiotherapy or medication that isn't safe for lactating mothers to take
- ▲ Hypoplasia of the breast also known as insufficient glandular tissue (IGT)
- ▲ A traumatic birth or postnatal period that made initiating feeding difficult or impossible

▲ An assault survivor who is triggered by breastfeeding
▲ A return to work that would not allow for pumping breaks
▲ A lack of breastfeeding support
▲ Postpartum stress or anxiety which made breastfeeding too steep a mountain to climb
▲ Low sense of worth or value

Even though I found breastfeeding my first three children a total breeze, I was served a tall glass of shut your mouth juice with my fourth child. Try as I might, my body refused. I was totally and utterly spent, caring for the other three young children. About six weeks in, it refused to co-operate. I remember the day I 'gave up' (see how loaded the language we use around breastfeeding is?). I was feeding my newborn baby in the bathroom while doing times tables with my eldest as I washed her hair. I was simultaneously treating my five-year-old's hair for nits and wiping my toddler's bum after an accidental whoopsie on the newly tiled floor. When the baby began screaming in hunger and frustration yet again, despite four weeks of support from a La Leche League lactation advisor, I made the agonising decision to stop. There hadn't been enough milk for a long time and no amount of rest (non-existent with four under six), natural supplements or middle-of-the-night alarm-setting and pumping were bringing it back.

I felt a total failure for not being able to feed my fourth baby for longer. I also felt so guilty that he was getting the shorter straw than his other siblings, who'd been fed up to the age of two. Now, six years on, I'm so grateful that I experienced the other side of the coin, because it gave me the opportunity to have compassion and empathy on a topic that had seemed pretty one-sided to me before. Thank goodness I learned in plenty of time before I began supporting a whole host of different mothers that it is never ok to judge or shame another mother into feeling that she hasn't done the best for her child. On a sidenote, Ted – the baby who got the least breast milk of them all – is the most healthy, strong, immune and content six year old. He sleeps and eats well (the weirdo likes sushi, radishes and roll mops), has an abundance of energy and a lovely gentle soul! His confidence in himself and his abilities is heart-warming to see. We are super bonded. Super close.

It isn't just formula-feeding mothers who need support. Adversity and judgement is faced by all mothers who feed their babies, no matter which way. Breastfeeding mothers also endure criticism, judgement and shaming for their feeding choices and are just as worthy and in need of support and understanding. Having been brought up in a body-confident family, I was well-equipped when a middle-aged man told me I should be feeding my baby in the toilet at a restaurant. Seething, I called the waitress over and asked her in the man's earshot to please pick up his plate and take it to the toilet so that he could eat his lunch there, seeing as he was asking me to feed my baby in a place of defecation. Don't let anyone shame you for how, where or how long you choose to feed. You are not responsible for how others respond to your feeding choices. Turn your shoulder to the shamers and whatever you do, don't be one of them.

Dream feeding

You might find it helpful (and quite possibly total and utter magic) to offer your baby a dream feed before you go to bed. A dream feed is a given around three to four hours after a baby has gone down for the night, usually around 10 to 11 p.m. It is initiated by a parent or caregiver, rather than the baby, and typically happens while the baby is asleep. There are several benefits to it:

△ Your baby's longest stretch of sleep is in unison with yours (preserving those crucial first five hours of your sleep)

△ Someone else can do it

△ It helps you feel confident that your baby won't be hungry for at least three hours (so 2 a.m. earliest. If you've been asleep since 9 p.m. that's five solid hours minimum)

Getting your first stretch of sleep in parallel with your baby's is smart because our brains are cleverly designed to prioritise the most restorative stage of sleep during the first few sleep cycles of the night. It is the first five or so hours of sleep that need to be solid. This is why, if you're woken before that, you feel like proper shit. A dream feed is the perfect way to protect those first few hours of your sleep (if someone else gives it so you can get to bed earlier). Many families swear by the dream feed. One study of 125 families found that babies who were dream fed slept longer at night. It's worth noting that the families who dream fed also put into place twenty other 'good sleep' recommendations such as using white noise and allowing infants to self-soothe so we can't be sure which of these approaches was responsible for the positive change. But we can be sure that the change was positive! In a much smaller study,[40] researchers asked thirteen families to follow three practices:

1. Give a feed to a newborn sometime between 10 p.m. and midnight

2. Gradually lengthen intervals between night feedings by trying alternative caretaking behaviours like changing a nappy and walking about with a baby or swaddling them

3. Make clear the difference between day and night by minimising social stimulation and artificial light at night

At eight weeks postpartum, all thirteen of the parents who practised this tri-approach reported that their babies were sleeping quietly and peacefully each night between midnight and 5 a.m. Sounds like a win to us – we'd have given anything for sleep like that at eight weeks!

Getting those solid five or six hours is absolutely life-changing! When Eve did this with her third baby (from three weeks of age) it was the best postpartum experience she ever had. Going to sleep after the 7/8 p.m. feed and not being needed again until 2 a.m. after six or so solid hours of sleep (and a chance for her boobs to stock back up) was a dream. People noticed how 'with it' she was; but more important than that, Eve felt the strongest in mind and body that she ever had following the birth of a baby.

DREAM FEED HOW TO

During a dream feed, enter the room quietly with the aim of keeping them asleep. You don't need to change a nappy overnight unless it is heavily soiled. But if your baby is really hard to rouse, a nappy change can be just the thing to get them just awake enough to feed. For some babies, popping your nipple or a teat into their mouth should stimulate a latch and the sucking reflex. This needs to happen in a safe feeding position in your arms and must not be done with them lying flat. There is rarely a need to wind them but do if you believe it's needed. If it's the only bottle feed of the day, either containing formula or EBM (expressed breast milk), you may find it helpful if someone other than the breastfeeding parent offers it. When it's an option to drink straight from the life-giving tap, very few babies will choose to have it decanted! When the wonder-tap is out of sight and smell, it's a much more appealing option. It also means you get a larger chunk of sleep. And your partner feels involved and purposeful. Win–win.

Let sleeping babies lie

Unless your baby is poorly, low birth weight, failing to thrive or you've been medically advised to do so, you don't need to wake them up in the night or in the middle of a nap to feed them. Allow them to show you what they are capable of sleepwise and try not to interrupt that if possible. Babies have been very cleverly programmed to wake for food and when they need you. They can't sleep through hunger. Or pain. Give your little one the benefit of the doubt and observe how much more capable they are than you give them credit for. Beautiful things happen when you can find the confidence to hold back and let them do what they are naturally able to do.

SLEEP BEGETS SLEEP

Another piece of advice that never fails to surprise parents is this; do not wake your baby or toddler up from their naps unless you have recent evidence that it disrupts future sleep. This advice is usually met with disbelief – *'How will my baby sleep at night if they take too much in the day?'* The reality is this: apart from the very few instances where waking them is a good idea, which we'll explain below, babies need enough day sleep to take their best sleep at night. Overtired babies are harder to settle, wired with adrenaline, hyperactive, super resistant to sleep and are more likely to wake up in the night and to wake early (pre-6 a.m.).

Typically, babies and toddlers need *more* sleep, not less. Sleep begets sleep. Try not to restrict day sleep unless you absolutely have to. We only have four instances when we wake a child from sleep. The rest of the time we let them take anything up to 2.5 to three hours at any one time.

The four occasions that we wake a child from sleep are if:

1. **It's beyond 7:30 a.m.** No one loves a lie-in more than a tired parent, but allowing your baby to sleep beyond that time usually makes the day skew-wiff (as our mum says) and this can throw off bedtime and night sleep (not worth the trade off!)

2. **A nap is creeping up to three hours in length.** Capping day sleep at three hours at any one time helps encourage the longer stretches of sleep to happen at night

3. **Bedtime will be negatively impacted on.** This usually only happens for children aged two and above. If they're not tired enough at bedtime, you'll need to lengthen the nap gap between their last sleep and bed (or drop the nap entirely). We'd recommend reducing the nap and doing it every other day, or a few times a week before you drop it entirely

4. **Your child is entering a nap transition** (we'll tell you more about this in our 'Resistance to Naps' section, in just a moment)

Sleep problems and solutions

Not being able to self-soothe/settle

Each week, exhausted parents reach out to us, desperate to understand why their children won't sleep. More often than not, they're baffled. Many feel they've tried everything. That they're in a good routine. That they feel they're doing 'all the right things' and just cannot fathom why sleep feels so hard. A lot of the time, their little ones depend on parental input for sleep to take place. Perhaps they 'need' to be fed/rocked/held/driven/pushed/co-slept with to fall or stay sleep. When this is the case, the whole family has probably come to believe that there really is no other way to do sleep. The thought of sleep happening without the boob/dummy/pram/bed-sharing feels impossible. When we tell the parents that the child doesn't *need* those things any more than they do, they think we're pulling their leg! These parents are desperate because what once worked no longer does. They want their little one to be able to sleep, but they just don't know how.

The good news is that we do know. You might remember that we talked earlier about the *ings*; how the way a baby is put to sleep directly impacts how they go on to sleep. When a baby comes into light sleep through the night (which we discovered earlier happens very regularly) they will need whatever they fell asleep to in the first place to be recreated if sleep is to continue. Either your child's sleep will be heavily dependent on your presence, or not. Once your child can take themselves peacefully off to slumber land, they'll breeze through their sleep cycles, perfectly able and happy to do sleep without any input needed from you. Allowing and enabling this life-skill directly results in peaceful nights (and happier days) for your baby and you.

HOW DO YOU KNOW WHETHER YOUR BABY CAN SELF-SOOTHE?

All babies and children who sleep more than forty-five minutes at a time *can* self-soothe. They're coming into light sleep that often, so if they get through any sleep cycles at all themselves, they can do it! But if most of the time you are intervening in their sleep, and doing it *for* them, you are likely to find that no matter what you do, your little one cannot do sleep alone. For most families who contact us, one of the following has to happen for sleep to take place:

△ A bottle or breast

△ Being rocked or bounced

△ Motion, such as in a pram or car

△ Contact napping

It's easy to see how associations such as the ones above are built. They are usually part of a wonderfully nurturing start to your baby's life during the fourth trimester. There wasn't (and still isn't) anything wrong with those things. But that doesn't mean that they can't become the very things that stand between you and the rest you need. Consider how as children we create patterns and behaviours that serve us. Later in our lives, we will have to find new ways of coping and living. We must unlearn the mechanisms that used to serve us but no longer do. This is a healthy evolution. A natural, respectful shedding of behaviours that no longer serve us. Rocking a newborn is a beautiful thing. Rocking a three-year-old, not so much.

Any *ing* that you use to get your child to sleep means that your little one is being *put* to sleep rather than taking themselves off to sleep. While doing sleep for your baby can feel the most natural and sustainable thing at first, if the opportunity for them to naturally fall asleep themselves is never practised or allowed, self-settling becomes a dormant skill. Use it or lose it, shall we say!

Take a baby aged eight months old who has always been fed to sleep. This happens for every sleep night and day since they were born. This means that they've received the message around four thousand times this is the only way sleep happens. That they need the boob/teat as their ticket to dreamland. There's nothing wrong with this if it results in brilliant sleep for you all, but the vast majority of parents tell us that it means sleep can't be done any other way and they feel as if their hands are tied. A baby who can only be fed to sleep isn't *unable* to self-settle, they simply haven't had the *opportunity* to learn or practise the thing they've been capable of all along. You have the power to enable this. You can lead them to better sleep. You only need to know how.

Solution
Self-settling can be gently introduced from the very beginning of life. When the time feels naturally right to you (for some families this can be any time between six to sixteen weeks of age) instead of doing sleep the usual way, you might like to aim to put your baby down sleepy but awake every so often. We recommend trying this at a good/ easy time of day, perhaps during the nap that your baby seems to resist the least (often the morning nap.) Putting them down for every sleep is not something you're aiming for at first. Even one independent nap every few days would be amazing at first! Using our Sleep Needs Table, find the nap gap and pop them into the cot with a full belly (we always feed/top up just before a nap). Try to pop them in drowsy but awake. It's fine if you want to rock, pat or cuddle beforehand to help them get closer to that finish line. Once they're sleepy but not asleep, place them gently into the cot.

One friend swore by placing a hot water bottle in the cot first as she was convinced it was the transference from warm and snuggly to cold and empty that woke her little one up. Give your baby up to twenty minutes to settle to sleep themselves, intervening only if they're clearly showing you they're unhappy. In which case, pick them up, soothe them and try again. You don't need to intervene if your baby does a frustrated grunt or shuffle – that just means they're working it all out. They are not distressed. Nevertheless, it can feel impossible to watch/allow. You'll most likely have an overpowering urge to *just quickly* tuck them back in/move their position/give them one more feed/check their nappy/re-swaddle them/close the blinds, etc. But all of this is unnecessary fussing. It's the kind of fussing that you simply don't have time for when you have other older children who need you to wipe their bum, pull Wotsits out of their nostril, get the Sudocrem off the sofa before your partner gets home. It's no coincidence that babies seem to get better and better at sleep as time goes on. It's because they've had the least interference!

So once your baby is in their cot, hold back. Resist the urge to rush in and rescue them. If you're finding it agonising, distract yourself with something. Remember that they're not asking to be saved. They're hardly screaming their heads off/sounding a siren or releasing a distress flare. They're just having a shift around and a vocalise as they work it out. Trust us when we tell you that if your baby needs you, they will let you know. Let them do that.

Once you've had success with them getting themselves off to sleep, even if the nap isn't the longest, celebrate it! Your little one just got themselves off to sleep, even for ten minutes! In allowing them to do so, you laid down one brick in the temple of peaceful sleep. And Rome wasn't built in a day, was it?! If it didn't work out this time, no dramas at all, Try to extend that nap in a way that works for your baby, such as a contact nap or buggy nap. Allow yourself to confidently have a go at trying out independent settling another time. If it doesn't happen for days, don't stress about it, or battle on for hours, just get them up or help them to sleep a bit more and consider it just one step along the way. The opportunity to self-settle can be offered to your baby before and after sleep. If you suspect they may still be tired or want a bit more sleep, try not rushing in as soon as they wake and seeing if they'll go back off. If they're going to, it'll probably be within twenty minutes.

If you don't want to go straight to trying independent sleeping, you can try to gradually reduce the amount of help you give them. If you rock them for fifteen minutes until they're asleep, try doing it for ten and seeing what happens when you place them gently into their cot with a little less input. Again, pick a good time of day to try this – perhaps a time that's going to be least stressful and most pressure-free for you and them. Providing opportunity without pressure or expectation is a wonderful way for your family to get to a place where the foundations for solid sleep can be gently laid down.

But even if you never got round to teaching your child how to self-settle, it is never too late. We work with children up to age six and there are other practitioners who work with children age six+ and teenagers. It is never too late to enable your child with solid sleep. And it is always worth it. It is a common misconception that the older the child, the harder it is to teach them. Children aged eighteen months to two years are often more straightforward cases because they can tell us how they feel and we can rule out hunger and other first year variables such as reflux. This age group is Eve's favourite to help support whereas Gem loves the first eighteen months cases.

If you tried self-settling in the past to disastrous effect, or you feel like you've tried everything without success and you're just not sure whether it can work for your baby or you, it is well worth you getting in touch with us to see if we think we can help you. We will only ever recommend our plans if we believe we can turn your sleep right around. We will tell you if we don't think our approach is a good match with yours or if we don't think it's the right time for you for whatever reason. The surest way to discover if we can help you is to ask. To discover which plan will get your family the sleep they need, take our two-minute self-assessment here: www.calmandbright.co.uk/find-my-plan.

Resistance to naps

Sod's law dictates that the minute you think you've figured out your baby's naps, a big shiny spanner comes flying out of nowhere and wedges itself right into the middle of your life. This might come in the form of your baby all of a sudden waking early from a nap or taking longer than they normally do to settle to sleep. It may also be that they are resisting sleep at a particular time of day. Or that they are refusing their second nap, which some parents incorrectly think means they're ready to drop it! Parents often find themselves in a bit of a 'nap nightmare' which often happens around the age of nine to fourteen months. All of the things we mentioned above are signs that your child's day sleep needs your attention. Naps can be really easily worked out, with the right tools. It's easy when you know the answer!

Solution

The very first thing we recommend to make naps lengthy, predictable and stress free is making sure that a baby or child can self-settle. Further to that, we don't advise waking a baby or toddler up from a nap unless in the four instances we outlined above. One of which is a nap transition, which happens around nine to fourteen months, when a baby is moving from two naps to one. The actual dropping of the nap takes place around fifteen to eighteen months but they are preparing for this for months (as many as ten months for some babies!). In the time leading up to the drop to one nap, you may find that your baby will start:

△ Waking early from the first or second nap

△ Resisting or refusing the second nap

△ Appearing not tired enough for the second nap

This can lead to frustration on both your parts because it's clear they're still tired but they won't sleep. Totally exasperating! When this happens, they're either gearing up for one nap or they're ready to drop it. The earliest we've heard of a successful drop to one nap is at eleven months, but most do it after fourteen months and before twenty-one months.

To help your baby prepare to take one long nap around the middle of the day, cap their morning nap at forty-five minutes, then use the three Fs (fresh air, fun and food) during their usual nap gap and then pop them down for their afternoon one with a lovely full belly. Let them take as long as they want within our three-hour limit (unless they're poorly, then let them take as long as they need, even beyond the three hours, as a one off). This simple adjustment should mean that they can continue taking two naps until they're ready to drop to one. You'll know the time is right to make the actual drop when despite capping the first nap, they still refuse the second one or begin to refuse the first. When you feel like you just can't fit the naps in, it's because you can't! It's time to drop one.

Know that bedtime can be any time between 6.30 p.m. and 7.30 p.m. (and as early as 6 p.m. and as late as 8 p.m. in emergencies like a danger nap or an overtired child!). You might like to use our Sleep Needs Table to work out the approximate gaps your child will need between sleeps and then go from there. Let's say you'd like your ten-month-old in bed by 7 p.m. To work out your day, you start twelve hours earlier. Three hours after 7 a.m. is 10 a.m. If he sleeps for forty-five minutes, he may well want to want to go down again around 2 p.m. and he may sleep for a couple of hours, meaning he'll be perfectly ready for bed around 7.

Try not to worry too much about any nap transition. Simply pick a day when your baby has had a good night's sleep and then create a longer gap before the one and only nap and put them down with a full belly around about four to five hours after they woke. When you first start on one nap, it might fall around about 11 a.m. (because they won't be able to last much longer), meaning that lunch needs to be given either before their nap or after it. Try not to stress about the fact that lunch is not at a 'normal' time and is instead at 11 a.m or 3 p.m. It matters not what you call the food you give them before or after they sleep, it's just about making sure that they're going down with a nice full belly so that when they do wake it won't be down to hunger.

Resisting naps may also be down to something physical bothering them (see Chapter Ten). Once you've ruled out anything physical, think about whether their sleep needs could be changing, using our Sleep Needs Table as a reference point. If they've been on the same naps for a long while, their naps will almost certainly need a bit of a shake-up. The nice and simple thing to remember about nap needs changing is that it can more often than not be remedied by keeping them up a little bit longer. When you think that you might need to make a change to the nap gaps, try extending the nap gap by about half an hour first. If that doesn't work, don't be afraid to keep trying different gaps until it clicks. Sometimes, the nap gap needs to shorten, especially if your child has been waking earlier or has been poorly recently. Remember, when it feels like you just can't fit the naps in, it means it's time to drop one! Don't worry that they're currently shorter naps and won't serve them if they're only having two – they're only short because they weren't tired enough, because they were on one too many naps. You'll soon find the naps lengthen when they're on the right number of naps.

When your baby goes down easily again for a nap, settles in their usual time, sleeps a nice length of sleep, wakes refreshed and is relatively happy between sleeps, you've found the right nap gap for now. Keep going with that until they tell you otherwise.

The four-month sleep regression

We've touched on four-month sleep regression earlier in this book, but it is such a pivotal moment in your child's sleep that we're going to delve a little deeper here. The four-month sleep regression is the one developmental event that we believe poses the greatest disturbance to your baby's sleep. While it can feel like you're back in the newborn days, it is in fact a progression. The disturbance comes from the maturation of your baby's sleep architecture. Unlike the sleep patterns in the first four months of life, which were inconsistent, at four months your baby's brain enables sleep to become dynamic. They will start to go through the sleep cycles that us adults do, making them capable of sleeping for much longer stretches (if of course they have the self-settling skills to do so). Their new forty-five-minute sleep cycles can pose a problem to babies who cannot yet self-settle, because however they have learned to do sleep becomes cemented at this point. Babies on our 0–5 month plan who can self-settle by the four-month mark rarely see much of a regression in sleep at all. Babies who are dependent on being put to sleep with an *ing* will at that point find it hard to sleep without it.

Solution
Self-settling is known as the Holy Grail for good reason. When it comes to the potential horror show that is the four-month sleep

regression, a baby who can self-settle will be able to link together their sleep cycles. If you reach the four-month mark without having enabled self-settling, it's certainly not the end of the world. We waited until after the five- to six-month mark with our children, before we had the tools to learn how to avoid it. If you're in the thick of the four month sleep regression, know that in just a few short weeks (by the five month mark) your baby will almost certainly be capable of sleeping eleven to twelve solid hours with one night feed, if you wish.

Bedtime battles

Once a child can self-settle, bedtime battles are usually reserved for parents of children age one and a half or older. Difficult bedtimes arise in response to something *within* your child or *around* them. The cause might be developmental, as they learn a new skill or adjust their day sleep needs. It may also be down to a change to their world as they know it. A new sibling, childcare setting, nursery start, or house move. Bedtime battles aren't much to do with bedtime, but they arise then because bedtime brings two significant factors. The first is 1:1 time with the parent (perhaps the first of the day) and the second is the inevitable separation from their parent for the night.

A child who might not have had much attention or quality time during the day may find themselves acting out. Sometimes, 1:1 time feels impossible. Perhaps you've had a hectic workday/a newborn baby to attend to/the period from hell or just plain old exhaustion ruining your life. Whatever the cause, bedtime is often the time for your child to try to get more of what they need from you and to delay separation with you. Please note, this can be just as much about them having the most brilliant, full and heart-filling day as it can be about not having had enough from you. The best days are harder to end, sometimes! There's no mother in the world that doesn't have a mixture of both kinds of days.

Whatever the reason for your child's bedtime battles, after a long day it can feel like the sprint at the end of the marathon. And many parents fall at this hurdle, starting calm but soon losing their temper and then feeling guilty for it. Perhaps you have ended the day cross with your child, to go on to vow that the next night will be different, and only to repeat the same patterns again? We know we have.

It may amuse you to hear (because it's so much funnier when it's not your child) some of the hilarious bedtime antics we've witnessed over the years. Together as a team, we've witnessed children:

△ Emptying the contents of every drawer in the room

△ Hiding in cupboards (with one child locking it from the inside!!)

△ Switching on and off the lights

△ Tying knots in cables

△ Hiding behind curtains (for the twenty seconds that we couldn't find them, it was anything but funny)

△ Telling their parents that they're hungry, thirsty, tired, not tired, need a poo, need another blanket, a drink or a dance

△ Singing 'We Three Kings of Orient Are' at the top of their lungs in the height of summer for two hours straight

△ Tying a dressing-gown cord to their door handle so they could open the door from bed. (The parents would rush in expecting to find him at the door, only to find him obediently in bed, grinning from ear to ear about how he'd outsmarted them. This one still makes us smile)

Solution

The first step to resolving bedtime battles is to identify what they're about. As we discussed earlier, they are usually some form of test, to check that they're safe and that you're certain. Sometimes, though, they can run a little deeper. For example, parents who work during the day may feel guilty about not being available, so they feel they have to make up for it at night. The guilt can also be linked into something less recent. You may have some feelings beneath the surface about being unavailable at some point for your baby (perhaps at some point in the postpartum period) and this can have an impact on how you feel about your availability today.

If you find it difficult to put healthy boundaries in place at bedtime, resulting in everything taking a lot longer than it needs to (with you rarely getting an evening to yourself) it might be an idea to unpick what's lies beneath your difficulties. Our psychological obstacles to sleep chapter (page 127) will help you to do this. Eve's poem is also a helpful thought provoker.

Spending what we call *golden time* with your child during the day, will help ease any guilt clouding your perspective at night. Golden time is very popular among our C&B families. It is a dedicated ten-to-twenty-minute daily slot of time which you give to your child. You can label it as anything you wish – perhaps find your own name that suits your child best. We've heard of superhero time, special Mummy and Daddy time and, the potential favourite, family fun time. Make this time sacrosanct. Treat it with the same importance as that business meeting or doctor's appointment that you've written in your diary *and* your phone. Maybe you've even ringed it with a highlighter if you found one with the lid still on! Make sure, when golden time happens, that your child has your full attention for those short few minutes a day. Be respectful of your child and your time together by making sure that you're device-free and fully present. Occupy your other children if possible. Let your child know that this time matters to you and that you are looking forward to it. Let your child decide what happens during golden time. Maybe they want to be quiet, calm, still and affectionate. Perhaps if your child likes to twiddle your hair or have their arm gently tickled at bedtime, this is a good time to do that. Maybe they want to create (paint, clay, draw). Or be more physical and active such as you chasing them, doing an aeroplane or playing horsies.

Golden time helps your child to understand that daytime is the time for cuddles, affection, fun, roughhousing and bonding. Nighttime, once a loving bedtime has ended, is for sleeping.

Try to avoid the urge to lead golden time, turning it into something you want to do. Let it be the one time of day when your child gets to call the shots completely. This means avoiding the urge to make a better suggestion or adapt their idea. As adults we lead all the time. This is an opportunity for them to have a go at being utterly in control and able to have a say in how they want to spend their time with you. We find after dinner is a great time for golden time, when their energy is all charged up. Try not to leave it until right at the end of the day when everyone is shattered. Not only does golden time benefit your child, it helps you to tick another item off the guilt list. Knowing that you've given a dedicated amount of one-to-one time to your child will help eradicate that nagging feeling that you haven't done *enough*. This will contribute to you feeling surer of your actions when bedtime comes around.

When tackling bedtime battles it's useful to negate your child's demands in advance. Pre-empt anything they're going to come up with; what factors they're going to think up as excuses to not sleep and negate them before you leave the room. For example:

'Here's your drink, so you won't need to wake Mummy or Daddy in the night for one.'

'You can have a wee at the last minute before bed and then we know you won't need another one before morning.'

'I know you sometimes get cold and ask me for another blanket so here's a lovely warm one at the end of your bed which you can easily pull up because you're so clever and able.'

If demands do surface in the night which you feel in your gut are an attempt to delay the onset of sleep, either don't engage with them or repeat a banal sleep phrase such as 'It's time for sleep now. I love you and I'll see you in the morning.' If they're begging you to allow them to go to the toilet again, you might want to simply point to the loo for them to attend, wait in silence while they do it/mess around for a minute and then lead them gently but confidently back to bed. You can bet your bottom dollar that nine out of ten times they didn't need to go at all, and it was just another bit of bait to see if you'll bite. In summary, bedtime battles are less about them being upset, or being a little shit just for fun. It's about them testing to see whether they really are safe and secure in your boundaries. It's about them saying through their actions, 'I'm unsure. Can you show me that you're not?

Tips to get started

We recommend after the bath staying upstairs until the morning. You might find it helpful to do things in a regular, predictable fashion. Try not to be too fearful of your child's resistance when you decide to take steps to change things. Start early to allow for some protest time if that's what you're expecting your child to do. It will help them greatly if you can work on not being too fearful of your child's resistance, however uncomfortable it might feel. Parents are rightly programmed to make their child's life as happy and as stress-free as possible and the very fleeting, short-term upset that comes with sleep teaching can feel like it's in conflict with our duty. But let us tell you this: the difficult moments (and they really are just moments in the grand scheme of things) are the golden keys to unlocking the door to a more rested life. It's only by getting out the other end of this super short-term struggle that you'll see the process for what it really is: a lesson in how to enable and empower your child to do something that will help them immeasurably. It's surely one of the greatest paradoxes that the most important lessons can be the hardest to teach.

While nobody wants to hear their child upset, it's not our job as parents to make everything ok all of the time. If we do that, what resources will they have when they need to go it alone at nursery or school, in a job interview or in a tricky situation? Reframing crying and upset before you embark on any sleep teaching can really help both you and your child. (We have a lot of resources on this for you on our Instagram page and website.) Fleeting and fast-fading protest is a far lesser problem than endless exhaustion. Our children deserve to experience the parents underneath all the fractious feelings. They – and you – deserve better.

Dreams and nightmares

Dreams and nightmares are very common in children aged three to six, with around half of children this age experiencing regular nightmares. In children age six to twelve, around two in ten will experience nightmares.[41] Nightmares usually happen during REM sleep (the final stage of sleep). This means that they're most likely to occur either in the middle of the night or in the early hours of the morning. Nightmares often first occur at pre-school age when children's worlds are changing and challenging them. This time sees them process lots of different emotions as they form new attachments and build trust with people outside of their family. This extra stimulation of their bodies and minds can send their wonderful imaginations and thought processes into overdrive, resulting in vivid dreams and sometimes nightmares. Extra reassurance might be needed at bedtime and children might go through a phase of waking in the night having remembered a dream or a nightmare and need extra reassurance and comfort until they're feeling secure enough to sleep again. Some things that can really help your child if they're experiencing nightmares are:

△ Lots of extra bonding time at home

△ Worry dolls or warriors – a wonderful tool to be used as part of a bedtime routine to help children verbalise and process their thoughts and feelings. Gem swears by them thanks to her job as a school nurse. Worry dolls can be bought for buttons at the online shop of your choice

△ A nice spritz of lavender on the pillow or your own homemade 'safe spray', which can be sprayed around the room before bed

△ Role play where a child can feel empowered and capable. You or one of their toys can be afraid and they can help you or them feel reassured. This in turn reassures them

Remember that dreams and nightmares are extremely common and are very much a normal part of development from the ages of three to twelve.

Night Terrors

Night terrors are very different from nightmares. For a start, they are experienced by far fewer children – around just 3 to 6 per cent. They typically happen in children aged three to eight and are episodes of complete panic and terror. They are thought to be caused in part by overtiredness. Some children display behaviours completely out of character and can scream, shout, sweat, appear terrified and be inconsolable and be in a trance-like state. This is very distressing for parents to experience, although it is far worse for them than the child – night terrors have no lasting psychological impact. They usually take place in the earlier half of the night[42] and typically last up to fifteen minutes. They can include sleepwalking and talking. The key difference between night terrors and nightmares is that night terrors are experienced while the child is asleep (despite their eyes being open) and they'll have no recollection of it the next day. The quickest way to differentiate between a bad dream and a night terror is to ask your child if they recall it the next day.

If your child is having a night terror, these things can help:

△ Wait the night terror out patiently and calmly, knowing that it will pass, and staying in close proximity to your child

△ Make sure your child is safe and doesn't get hurt by thrashing around

△ Do not wake your child or try to reason with them. If you do, they are likely to be disorientated and confused and this may increase their agitation

△ Children will usually settle down and return to sleep on their own within a few minutes.

There is no treatment for night terrors, but you can help prevent them by creating a bedtime routine that is relaxing and by meeting your child's emotional needs in the waking hours. Make sure your child gets the rest they need by ensuring they're on the unbroken eleven to twelve hours sleep that they need overnight. Our recommendations in the nightmare section can help with night terrors, too. If your child is suffering from recurrent night terrors, we advise seeking help from your local GP, who may refer you to a sleep clinic. You can also reach out to your local school nurse for support and guidance.

CHAPTER TWELVE

SLEEP AND YOU

By the time your path crossed with this little book, you may have had months or years of broken sleep under your belt. Or maybe your child's sleep was a while back but you're yet to come down from being on high alert for so long. Perhaps your child's sleep fills you with such anxiety that you're genuinely concerned you'll never sleep again. In this chapter we're going to guide you through the things that can help and support *your* sleep. We'll talk to you about the rollercoaster of different emotions you might experience once your non-sleeping baby sleeps through. We'll discuss self-acceptance and how mothering yourself helps you mother others better. We're going to tell you wholeheartedly that you are worthy of restorative, reparative sleep, just as your children are. We'll help you come to terms with accepting your new reality of better. We're going to dive a little bit into vulnerability and parental sleep anxiety and explain how you have the power to make sleep better. We'll also touch on some evidence-based sleep hygiene and give you all the tools we have to help you improve your sleep. Because what's the use of your kid sleeping if you can't?!

Feelings

While everyone's experience of sleep teaching is different, the feelings that families face as they journey through it are strikingly similar. Over the years it has helped parents to know that they are united in their feelings with countless others. We've listed some of the most common feelings parents tell us they've faced, using real comments from real parents, before, during and after the sleep teaching.

Before

vulnerable – *I don't know who to trust or which way to turn*

despairing – *I've given up hope*

fearful – *what if it doesn't work?*

hopeless – *we are beyond help*

helpless – *my child will never sleep*

guilty – *it's my fault*

anxious – *I'm obsessing over sleep and where I'm going wrong*

overwhelmed – *I don't know where to start*

sceptical – *are these people promising the earth just to get my money?*

doubtful – *it may work for others, but it won't work for us*

desperate – *I can't go on like this*

confused – *maybe if I just try this again first, I'm sure that worked once*

lost – *how do I know what to do?*

During

shocked – *did my baby really just sleep for eleven hours straight?*

disbelieving – *this can't be true*

overwhelmed – *this is too much to compute*

hopeful – *could it really be that we're going to have sleep in our lives?*

fearful – *what if it doesn't last?*

wary – *it's early days, surely it can still go backwards?*

cautious – *I'm not getting too excited just yet*

tentative – *it's only four nights of solid sleep, still time for it to go wrong*

nervous – *what about naps when we're out and about?*

excited – *I just woke up naturally, by myself!*

hopeful – *life feels brighter*

enlightened – *everything has fallen into place*

After

gobsmacked – *we are speechless!*

elated – *I feel on top of the world*

proud – *I did that. I taught her how to take the sleep she needed!*

relieved – *we don't have to live like that any more*

amazed – *I keep having to pinch myself*

energised – *I've just signed up for the local 5k run I've always wanted to do*

empowered – *I feel so much more connected with my child and needs now*

relaxed – *we'll figure it out later*

playful – *who wants a ride on the Mummy train?*

clear-headed – *I feel so much more connected with who I am and what I want to do with my life*

present – *look at those colours in the sky!*

connected – *I've never felt more connected to my child*

joyful – *life is GOOD*

grateful – *we can't believe this is our reality*

Mixed emotions

As you can see, a huge range of emotions can unfold as you navigate your way to a better life. This is part of the reason why we offer 1:1 support. As well as providing the 'how to' – we are there to help you process the big feelings. For a handful of parents, their feelings don't unfold in the order described above. Every so often a parent will still feel some of the feelings in the 'before' section even after perfect sleep has taken hold. This is because they are still plagued with the remnants of the fears and anxieties they experienced before. They aren't flooded with elation at the first (or fifth) twelve-hour night. They are too worn down by what has passed before. While these parents are in the minority, it's important to talk about them. These parents take longer to accept and believe and hope.

When we first started doing this all those years ago, we didn't have the experience or advanced emotional toolkit we needed to understand why parents sometimes felt this way. On the surface it seemed hard to understand. They had solid sleep now. They had what they asked us of us. Why weren't they overjoyed? We soon learned.

We have held space for every feeling every parent has felt since we began our work. No feelings are unwelcome or misplaced. It's very much a process. Parents who experience joy later often feel bad, saying, 'I *should* feel happy, so why don't I? I thought that as soon as sleep was fixed in my family that everything would be instantly better.' We always explain that sometimes the joy comes later for good reason. The longer sleep deprivation has taken hold, the longer it's been able to wreak its havoc. Earlier on, we talked about the impact it has on our brains and bodies and this isn't always overcome in a few days. Sometimes, parents need more time to recover. They need to protect themselves from ever going back to where they once were. Once solid sleep is enabled, a full acceptance of that requires great vulnerability. If parents allow themselves to dare to believe in their new norm, it means if it gets taken away it will hurt even more. They'll be falling from a higher height if it all goes wrong.

But rarely does it all goes wrong. In fact, it's practically unheard of. Sure, parents will encounter future sleep hurdles, for they're part and parcel of life. But once solid sleep reigns, it can bend and shift a little bit, but like an ancient oak tree in a storm, it can't be broken. Its roots run too deep.

We want you to know that it's ok if you feel a sadness when one phase ends and another begins. Feeling sad about what *was* does not mean that what *is* isn't right. It's perfectly normal if a part of you feels sad that your baby or toddler no longer depends on you at all hours of the night. This doesn't mean that you want to return there. Sleep deprivation sucks. It's like missing an ex who was no good for you. They may have done a mean spag bol, but they were impossible to live with! Parenthood is laced with tiny beginnings and beautiful endings at each and every turn. As one door closes, another one opens. We can mourn the loss of each fleeting phase while we celebrate the beginning of another.

It'll get better itself

At the beginning of our baby's life, we all expect broken nights. The early weeks and months of parenthood are made up of the tiniest stints of sleep, just as they should be. But soon enough, our baby is half a year old and still not sleeping. A year comes. Still no sleep. At this point they've been on solids for a few months and broken nights still rear their ugly head. You tell yourself it's a phase/leap/teeth/anything to give you a reason, some semblance of control. Then they're eighteen months, 1.5 years old. A toddler. You tell yourself it'll get better once they've learnt to crawl/walk/start nursery/move into their own room or a big bed. Then they're approaching pre-school age and sleep is yet to be solid. Before some parents can say sleep deprivation, they realise that their 'baby' is starting school in September and has yet to sleep through the night!

Low self worth

When you embark on your journey to sleep, the focus is usually on your baby – getting them the sleep they need. Some parents, particularly those who are suffering with low self-worth because of the exhaustion, find it hard to consider that this is for them, too. Isn't it so much easier to do something good for your baby than for yourself? Many parents have failed to prioritise their own rest for the best part of for ever. They've put themselves at the bottom of the list. But most parents know deep down that they're not living their best life when they're exhausted. The parents we help soon realise that giving their child a rested parent was just as important as getting their child their own rest.

Low reserves

It takes real courage to make changes to sleep. Parents are required to dig deep and that takes hard work and dedication, something that many will feel they don't have while operating on low reserves.

Before we begin a sleep support with a family, we talk about things potentially being tougher short term, but how it is all for the greater good. That if they can just get over that start line, they're going to have more energy than they ever imagined. We understand better than anyone how tempting it is to do the easiest thing in the moment. To just give them that quick feed/rock/bottle. You know it'll work there and then, and you're too tired to think past the here and now. The reason why so many of us operate on 'short-term gain, long-term pain' mode is because we simply don't have the reserves to do anything else. We also don't have the mental clarity to think of an alternative way, or to analyse the merits or shortfalls of what we're doing. We are in survival mode.

We help parents to step out of the here and now just for a moment, to help them understand that they have two choices when struggling with sleep. They can either continue to do the 'short-term gain, long-term pain' option which perpetuates broken sleep and keeps them stuck in a situation that isn't working for them or their family. Or, they can dig deep, bravely choosing instead (with our support and encouragement and a whole new set of skills), the short-term difficulty in return for immeasurable long-lasting gain. Once you realise that it can be just a few days before you're on the other side, you will find it within yourself to take control of the uncontrollable. To find hope in what has felt hopeless for a long time.

We know first-hand how when you're standing at the bottom of the mountain, you're not thinking of the view at the top, but rather the slog to get there. But we can promise you this – with our hands crossed over our hearts – that the view at the top is worth the slog. And you don't have to climb it alone. We're right behind you.

Vulnerability

We've talked a lot about vulnerability in this book. About how changing life for the better always requires some of it. The more you allow yourself to believe that solid sleep can become and remain your new norm, the more your confidence will grow. Dr Brené Brown, a research professor at the University of Houston, has spent the last two decades studying courage, vulnerability, shame and empathy. (If you haven't watched her TED Talk on the power of vulnerability, then put the darn book down and go and watch it. We can always wait for Brené!) She talks so eloquently about vulnerability and this particular quote of hers feels very fitting to place here:

> To believe in something with your whole heart, to celebrate a fleeting moment in time, to fully engage in a life that doesn't come with guarantees. These are risks that involve vulnerability and often pain. But recognising and leaning in to the discomfort of vulnerability teaches us how to live with joy, gratitude and grace – @brenebrown.

So not only is it ok to feel vulnerable but it's also necessary. If you are to let in the light of a rested life, you're going to have to believe it's possible. Allow hope, excitement and anticipation about the life that lies ahead to creep in. Brighter days are coming, just as soon as you believe they can exist.

Parental sleep anxiety

This, my friends, is a proper *thing*. We didn't know it was a thing before it became a thing (for both of us) and now it's something that we regularly support mothers with. Perhaps you've been there alongside us in the past (or even now); worrying whether your children are ok when they sleep for longer than you expect, having your life ruled by your baby's naps, wanting to punch anyone in the face who is noisy while they sleep, obsessing about getting sleep *right*, watching the monitor like baby TV?! A telling sign that always makes us recognise we have some kind of anxiety going on when we have the chance to sleep but can't. Eve remembers hitting her real-life rock bottom one morning after a series of nights from hell and after her husband took all four out of the house for three hours so she could sleep, not being able to. The sheer frustration and anxiety of not being able to sleep even when your baby does leaves parents feeling defeated, exasperated and hopeless.

We talk a lot about habitual wakes in children, but we too can wake from habit. The odds are that your body has long been pro-grammed by a cute but very expensive alarm clock and, as a result, you're probably used to waking at ungodly hours. A change to this, especially a sudden one such as the kind our plans can bring, is a physical shock to the system. Emotionally, it's a huge transition, too. Most parents need a bit of help getting their own sleep back on track after being on high alert for so long. Here are our tried and tested techniques to help ease parental anxiety and aid adult sleep.

Worth

While this might feel like we're going in *way* too deep and hard for a Tuesday night (or whenever it is for you), the truth is you're not going to prioritise sleep unless you believe you're worth it. Let us save you some time here. You are. Adequate rest is a birth right (along with joy, peace and love). You are worthy of proper rest. Read that again and say it yourself, out loud now (told you we were bossy):

I deserve proper rest

If you don't believe you're worthy of good things, you may find yourself in a pattern of self-sabotaging that new-found sleep. While we appreciate that this sounds an utterly bonkers thing to suggest, it happens. Both of us have done it on some level. It looks like this: despite efforts to change, parents keep finding themselves slipping back to old ways when it comes to sleep. (Note that this isn't always self-sabotage, it may be a lack of confidence or a really rough run of physical health obstacles that require extra comfort. This is different of course and we have given you lots of tools to help you overcome health obstacles to sleep earlier on in the book.) Sometimes, though, self-sabotage rears its head when parents:

△ Do not believe deep down that they are worthy of proper rest

△ Don't actually want the changes to happen (subconsciously)

△ Don't believe in sleep teaching and seek to create evidence to support their belief

△ Are fearful of what better sleep will mean (their partner coming back into bed/the energy to finally write that book/ leave that job/run that marathon) all of which present opportunity for failure/pain

△ Subconsciously want to maintain their children's dependency on them which affirms their worth and value in the mother role

△ Don't want sleep to be sortable within a few days because if it was so easy to fix why couldn't they do it themselves?

△ Want to place blame elsewhere for sleep being so bad

When we're supporting a family, if we are conscious that any sort of self-sabotaging might be happening, it's never met with judgement. The practice of self-sabotage is linked so closely with self-worth that parents need to be met with kindness, nurture and understanding to help them get the message that they are worthy of support and help. Your children are deserving of good sleep and all of the gifts that brings. And so are you.

Build your own village

This book has being written during the global pandemic of COVID-19. Today, as we live isolated lives, mothers are finding it harder than ever to access the supposed village it takes to raise a child. In the absence of the usual support networks that were available to parents pre-COVID-19, we need to mother ourselves and each other now more than ever. Learning how to do this in practice can make a big difference to how life feels and how we function in it. In order to meet our own needs, we first need to know what they are. A great way to do this is to learn how to hold space for ourselves.

Hold space for yourself

Now more than ever, holding space for yourself couldn't be more important. Eve always used to think the concept a bit naff, but she totally gets it now (lockdown, with an ever-growing business, four children who needed to be home schooled and a book to write gave her a crash course on its importance!). This can feel quite hard to do when you're putting everyone else's needs, wants and feelings before your own (as we are led to believe *good* mothers do!) but paying attention to how *you* feel and what *you* need can help you to level-up, tune in to where you're at and give yourself space and time to fill up your own bucket. How can you fill everyone's cup when you've not been to the wellness well to top up your own bucket first? For us, holding space is about doing anything that honours the one person who has complete power over how you experience your days. If you can't justify holding space for yourself for your own benefit, view it as an act of generosity and commitment to the ones you love. Here are some of our favourite ways to honour ourselves:

△ Be still. Breathe in peace/healing/light/love/acceptance/ gratitude. Breathe out anger/regret/resentment/hostility/ guilt/fear

△ Observe how you are feeling (without judgement)

△ See yourself as a friend would, with compassion and without judgement or criticism

△ Ask yourself what you need on a daily (if not hourly) basis

△ Nurture thoughts and actions that help you to feel most like yourself

△ Be the perfect example for your children to learn from by being true to your authentic self

△ Tweak your daily behaviour to align with your values

△ Confidently create boundaries free from guilt

△ Do something that the little girl within you loves to do

Love yourself

A loving parent will encourage their child to be their truest self. They'll congratulate them on every small achievement, let their imaginations run wild, encourage them to dream as big as possible and forgive them when they get it wrong. When their child falls down, they'll pick them back up and encourage them to try again with gentle words of encouragement. This is just how we must treat ourselves. We must mother our *inner* child as we'd parent our outer child. You might describe yourself as scatty and disorganised, but a friend might say you were super creative, fun to be around and always there in times of need. You might say you're obsessively organised and too uptight. A friend may say you are someone who never forgets the important things and thinks far enough ahead to get spaces on all the fun things for the kids. View yourself with the same love a friend would. With the same love you'd offer your child. Mother Teresa once said, 'If you want to change the world, go home and love your family.' We want to take it one step further: To change the world, go inwards and love yourself.

Buddha said:

You can search through the entire universe for someone who is more deserving of your love and affection than you are yourself and that person is not to be found anywhere. You, yourself, as much as anybody in the universe, deserve your love and affection.

It is perhaps hardest to tune in to and love ourselves when we are on our absolute last legs. But this is when we need to do it most. There is no one way to do this, because we all find different things relaxing and beneficial.

Most nights, Eve lies on her acupressure mat and breathes deeply (she has to, to work thorough the pain of the 4000 spikes on her bare skin!!). When her nervous system settles down and the blood rushes to the surface of her skin, it warms and calms her. Forced into the moment by the physical sensations, she then lets her brain catch up, and usually gives thanks for what she's grateful for that day (sometimes through gritted teeth, admittedly). After that, she does a check in with herself. She brings focus to the areas (physical or mental) that feel in need of some attention or care. She asks herself what she needs to do more or less of tomorrow.

Gem holds space for herself in a different way. For her, it's less of a ritual and more about sneaking moments just for her within the crazy every day. That might be taking herself off to the loo for five deep breaths or a cry. It might be taking the time to fill up that bottle of water for herself when she does her children's drinks for the day and adding some Rescue Remedy in it on those really tough mornings.

It's brushing your teeth and being present for those two minutes and telling yourself how well you're doing, rather than staring straight ahead in a zombie-like stare. It can be putting your feet up with a hot cup of tea for five sacred minutes and telling the kids that they can talk to you again when the cup is empty. It can be sitting down and listening to a podcast for ten minutes. Or crumbling on the kitchen floor and having a good old weep. Sometimes, on those bonkers busy days, it can be just pausing for a moment where you are, turning your palms up to the sky, taking some deep breaths and finding your feet again.

Forgiveness

Think how freely we forgive our little people each and every day. We do this because they're learning as they go along, are bound to make mistakes and are doing the best they can. Yet aren't we doing just the same? We're so much harder on ourselves than on them. But we are just little people who have gone on to raise our own little people without a manual in sight. Like our parents before us, we are doing the best we can with the tools that we have. Yet we are our own worst critic. Forgiving ourselves for the times we aren't our best selves is imperative for us to feel good enough to dare to try again. Choose every day to forgive yourself. Give yourself permission to be perfectly imperfect. Know that every single day is a blank canvas. Know that your best is good enough.

Acknowledge all of the little wins through the day if you can (write them down if it helps) and remember that the little stuff *is* the big stuff. If all you did today was get out of bed to do breakfast for your little people and collect them from school or nursery, you showed up. Fish fingers for tea is a win. A peaceful story time is a win. Getting one load of laundry on is a win. And sometimes, just getting through the day is enough.

Healthy sleep habits

When it comes to improving your own sleep, we have you covered. We are going to guide you through the incredibly simple things that have helped us and the families we support to get sleep back on track.

Start each day with five intentional breaths

Told you. Easy peasy. When we say to you that this has been a total game changer for us, we aren't kidding. We change the intention each day depending on what we want to summon that day. It might be patience, courage, clarity of mind, authenticity or self-protection. Get out of bed and sit on the side of it for a few moments as you take five conscious breaths in and out. This simple activity kickstarts our parasympathetic nervous system (which acts as a break to any stress response) setting you off on the right footing for the day. Don't knock it until you've tried it for three consecutive days!

Gentle exercise

We are about as far from gym bunnies as you could get. So while you go for your life and do whatever floats your boat movement wise, we are talking here about gentle exercise such as taking a stroll down the road (with a sleeping babe in tow in the buggy if you need to, and why not pick up one of your favourite drinks on the way home?). It only needs to take five minutes to have a little stretch. Or putting on your favourite song and dancing around the kitchen (this is Gem's favourite). It's moving. Movement can really shift your energy. Your body will love you a little bit more for it and those magic endorphins that are released afterwards are a lovely little bonus.

Nature

Nature has so much potential to help us to sleep. Fresh air each day is a gentle sigh of relief for the body and mind. And bright light is a sign for it to keep active and awake. Lavender is renowned for its relaxing properties for good reason. We love nothing more than a few drops of it on a pillow or in a bath. Magnesium rubbed into the soles of your feet or sprinkled into your bath can really help, too. You might have your own natural remedies that you love. Lavender, Rescue Remedy and lemon balm sleep chews are three of our favourites.

Wind down

Don't expect to dive into bed and for sleep to just happen with the click of a finger. Falling asleep is a physiological process. Think of it almost as a descent to sleep that's needed. Take at least thirty minutes to unwind before you go to sleep each night. This is best in darkness, or in dim light. Create a little ritual of activities that help you wind down. We love things like journalling, taking a magnesium bath, listening to some calming music, and a meditation or a podcast. Or silence. Silence after a noisy day really is golden.

Unplug

Computers, phones and tablets emit blue light. This suppresses our body's natural melatonin, the hormone that helps us to fall asleep. Unplug confidently. Try charging your phone outside your room for one night and see how it feels. It might surprise you how liberating it is.

CHAPTER THIRTEEN

SLEEP HEALS

Perhaps when you first heard about this book, you raised a cynical eyebrow and a snarled top lip. Perhaps you even rolled your eyes at the claim that any baby or child aged six months to six years could sleep eleven to twelve solid hours if only they were given the chance. Maybe your feelings against sleep training or controlled crying were so strong that you wanted to read this book to a) assure yourself that sleep teaching was the stuff of the devil or b) explore whether something that had seemed so abhorrent could in fact set you free. Whatever your reason for seeking our words out, we hope they have offered you a glimmer of clarity. Hopefully, you now know that you should never feel guilty for choosing to sleep teach, any more than you should feel guilty for choosing not to. You should also be aware by now that the sleep struggle is not mandatory. That you have the ultimate power to end it, should you want to. It is you and not fate who decides how tired you are and for how long. Never again do you have to feel like no one else will ever understand how punishing exhaustion is, or that you are alone in how you feel. Every parent we've ever met has walked their own version of the same jagged path as you. Every one of them has found it impossible at times, however much the glossy online pictures suggest otherwise. Back when we were breastfeeding our babes by the light of the moon, feeling painfully isolated and alone, we found it comforting to think of all the other mothers who basked and swayed with their babes under the same moonlight. Dazed and exhausted and resentful and besotted. It was as if the moonlight connected us at a disjointed time. The women in the moonlight stand alongside you at this moment. And so do we. We hear you and we see you. We honour your struggle, and we have written this book to raise you up from it.

No rush

You should now feel safe in the knowledge that broken sleep in the early weeks and months is completely normal. That there is no rush to get your baby sleeping through the night (because they're not supposed to at first) and that there's no such thing as bad habits. Instead, the first few months can freely be a time of submission; of riding the waves rather than swimming against them. Anchor yourself to the acceptance that each day you will feel differently (sometimes within the same hour) and that's ok. Don't let the fear of building a rod for your own back steal away those irreplaceable, fleeting first moments. Those moments – the way their head fits perfectly into your neck, the way the light catches his lashes – are what it means to be alive. Soak those moments up. Breathe in those heavenly scented heads. Cast aside the *shoulds* and surrender to what *is*. Remember that there are no rights or wrongs, only what *feels* right and what *feels* wrong. If it feels right and good to co-sleep, feed to sleep, baby-wear to sleep, rock to sleep or do anything else to help support your baby or child to sleep, then do it! If your baby is six months or sixteen months (or for that matter six years) when you choose to enable sleep (or indeed if you choose never to enable it at all) then you're right on track.

Wider lens

We hope that you can look at sleep with a wider lens. You should have an understanding that sleep teaching is not about leaving them to it or implementing strict routines that leave you feeling like you've failed. It's about watching your baby over the clock and being led by them and not some archaic textbook. It's about giving them the opportunity to practise something they've been perfectly capable of all along. You are now equipped with all the information you need to discover the true obstacles that stand between you and a full night's sleep. You should now understand that there is no one size fits all. No one formula to throw at the *problem*. With any luck, you'll have discovered that there isn't a problem after all. Just another way to do sleep, should you want it.

You have the power

You do not need us to rescue you. You are no damsel in distress. You are a powerful, capable, knowledgeable person underneath the doubt. You have the most expertise on your child and a sure inner knowing about what is best for them, if only you trust yourself more. We do not have the power when it comes to sleep. You do. You are the person you need. You can overcome any sleep challenge you face. All you need is a well kitted-out tool belt so you can choose how best to tackle it. We have been where you are now and we know how it feels to have absolutely nothing left to give. We know how hard it is just to decide what to cook for tea some days and how even getting dressed or washing can feel like too great a task some days. We know how you can feel deeply in love with and thankful for the children in your arms in one moment while screaming inside for them to leave you alone/shut up/go the f*ck to sleep the next. But feeling monstrous doesn't make you a monster. It just means you're tired. We know it can feel impossible to muster up the courage and energy that's needed to make changes to sleep. How it can almost feel easier to just keep it as it is, even if that feels unbearable too. But if you keep on taking the easy route (spoiler: it soon ends up being anything but easy) you sign yourself up for continued, long-term struggle. Short-term gain for long-term pain. If you can switch it up to choose short-term pain (a bit of work and doing things differently) you will receive immeasurable, long-lasting gain. You discredit yourself if you think that you don't have it in you to do this. Think how much you get through and accomplish each day on little to no sleep. Can you even imagine what you are capable of when your body and mind is rested?!

Sleep heals

For just a moment, picture a mother who you don't yet know. She is worn and weary; battered and bruised by too little sleep for too long. Although she wears a smile on her face for her family, it doesn't reach her eyes. She is giving all she has but still it is not enough. She is bone tired and doesn't know how she can carry on. Is that mother worthy of proper rest? If she is, then aren't you? You and your child are worthy of a rested life. You have the right, just as much as anyone else on this earth, to claim your nightly chance to restore, recoup, repair and recover. It is not selfish to want in on the magic of sleep. It is, after all, the ultimate healer and life-enhancer. When we honour our bodies with adequate rest, our minds are free to do what they do best: to dream, solve, hope, create and connect. Solid sleep cures the body, heals the mind and soothes the soul. It is the fuel that powers an authentic life, one where we can show up as our truest and best selves. Not only do we benefit from this, everyone we love does, too.

More than sleep

In the last year, a newly rested mum called Sophie told us that she thought our work didn't have much to do with sleep. It stumped us at first – wasn't sleep *exactly* what we did?! She explained that while the physical rest was heavenly, it was the *life that sleep enabled* which was where the magic was found. Sophie felt she was better equipped to handle anything life threw at her now that she was no longer ruined. She told us that a lot of the time, she was able to be the mother she always dreamed of being and that, even better, on the days when she wasn't that mother, she was able to release any guilt about it, simply starting afresh the next day. It turns out that Sophie wasn't alone in her thinking. Her voice joined a sea of others from around the world who told us how what they'd got from the plans was so much more than sleep. We went back through years of messages, cards, emails and notes to find some of the most remarkable words that were shared with us so that we could share them with you now.

You woke me up in more ways than one. I am a surgeon who before the sleep teaching was not safe to drive to work, let alone operate. We are now five years into twelve-hour nights and I can honestly say it was the best decision I have ever made as a parent

I thought I was a cynical and sceptical person, but I was just knackered. I'm much more positive (and fun) now

I have so much confidence in my ability to read my little girl now

My bond with my little one has deepened ten-fold because I am 'there'

I'm sure I don't need to go into much more detail than to say that my husband is VERY pleased I am now rested!!

I thought I had an unhappy baby, but he was just shattered

The resentment I used to feel overnight has disappeared. I now enjoy our rare overnight being needed times

I would never have had another baby if it wasn't for C&B

You took me from rock bottom to standing tall

My friends have commented on how much brighter I am

I no longer forget the things or people that matter to me

Can't tell you how good it feels to know that I did this!! Me! You didn't come in and do it for me. There was no magic wand. I did it!

My only complaint is that I was late for work!! I've not needed an alarm for over a year but this morning she slept to 8! Money back, please!!

I never bought a plan, but your and Gem's words brought me back from the edge more times than I can say

You flagged an undiagnosed CMPA on our first conversation

I used to think I was a bad mummy as none of my three children slept. You showed me I'm the best mummy for them in the world

I am now the mum I always wanted to be

Rosie's story

I hope it's not too gushy. I'll never be able to thank you enough for everything. I am so so grateful. You are my hero. (I think you're superwoman. Are you??!)

I am a different person to the one I was a week ago, in every single way and I am certainly a better mummy. Days before starting this programme I hit rock bottom and ended up at the doctor's in floods of tears feeling like I couldn't cope with life any more. The doctor diagnosed me with PND and prescribed me medication.

Sleep was awful, my baby was waking every hour at night to feed. Every morning, I woke in a state of panic about the day ahead. My baby depended on me to rock/feed her to sleep and sometimes this didn't work, meaning no sleep for anyone!

I wasn't sure I had the strength to start the programme, I felt so low, however, confidence was instilled in me by Eve and Gem to go ahead, they treated me like one of their family – such incredibly kind ladies. We bought the 'Hand in hand' programme and I was introduced to Lucy – my hero, who held my hand every step of the way. She is the best teacher I have ever had and I am so incredibly lucky to have been nurtured and supported by her. Right from the start she was my rock, reassuring me I could do it, and filled me with confidence throughout the process.

Almost instantly my baby was settling herself to sleep and within two days sleeping through the night. I still can't believe it. I am the old me again, everyone has noticed and no medication has so far been needed. WE ARE SLEEPING!!

We will never be able to express our gratitude to you, Calm & Bright – you have changed our lives.

WE LOVE YOU ♥♥♥

Mark (Rosie's husband)'s story

When my wife first suggested that we may need to pay for an external influence to sleep teach our six-month-old, I was dubious to say the least. I really and truly could not have been further from the truth, with the endless support from Calm & Bright genuinely changing the lives of the three of us.

The service from Lucy has been nothing short of extraordinary. Always on hand with WhatsApps, voice notes, phone calls and everything in between, it has felt like she has been here holding our hand through the process. She has championed our every move, decision and supported us through, instilling a confidence in us around sleep and parenting in general which used to be dreaded!

The change I have seen in my wife is miraculous; she has returned to being the same confident person she always has been and the difference in her approach to sleep time and life in general couldn't be more different.

To any parents contemplating investing in help with baby sleep – Calm & Bright are the way, do not even think twice. It will certainly turn out to be the best decision you've ever made.

It's been incredibly moving to look back over the things that people have said over the years about what a life with sleep has meant to them. It's been deeply cathartic writing the words we longed to hear all those years ago. This is the book that we wish had been placed gently into our shaking hands, back when we believed there was no other way. Back when we thought we had to choose between brutal sleep training and surviving on brutal levels of sleep. There wasn't even a glimmer of hope back then, just a fog of conflicting information which we staggered about blindly in, until we dropped to our knees in surrender. It is precisely because of that stumbling, that surrender, that staggering mess of a journey, that we are so well equipped to be your guides on your quest to solid nights and happier days. We are so grateful that we were given the opportunity to turn our mess into our message.

If we achieve nothing else in this life, we will rest easy if the words within this book can free even one family from the grim grip of despair. But if we were being greedy, our hope would be that our words might forge a tiny bridge of peace between the opposing sleep camps of our time. Because the sooner that we realise that we're all in different boats but weathering the same storm, the better. We are all blagging it, shitting it, ballsing it and wondering when the hell we'll find out what it's all about. (Let us know when you find out, will you?) Try to be kind to that mum at the opposite end of the sleep debate. She's doing the best she can with the tools she has. Just like you. Peace begins with you. When you are sure of yourself and your chosen path, you won't need others to feel the same way to validate your truth because truth exists of its own accord. Make peace with the path you choose and allow others to walk their own.

Imagine

Imagine for a moment that we are handing you a piece of paper. On it is written the exact number of minutes, hours, days, weeks, months and possibly even years that you have struggled with sleep. Now picture yourself during that time. Are you pacing the floor at an ungodly time of night? Searching frantically online for answers? Shouting until you see their little lips wobble and then weeping with immense guilt? Are you driving or walking around with gritted teeth just to force a nap? Holding on to them longer when they hug you so that they don't see that you're crying? Wondering if you're the problem? Why you seem to struggle more than other mums? Now imagine all that time and energy focused elsewhere; on the people, places and things that matter most. Imagine that you're not only going to have that time back, but you're going to be rested enough to enjoy it. Can you dare to imagine your future rested self right now? Maybe she's pushing that swing with true playfulness and joy rather than with gritted teeth and glazed-over eyes. Maybe she's finally *there*, to really feel the firsts and the lasts. Maybe she feels good enough about herself that when she gets it wrong, she forgives herself generously. Perhaps she's living with purpose, gratitude and hope. Maybe she feels more like herself than she ever has. Perhaps she is not as far out of reach as you may think. Maybe she's been right there all along, waiting patiently beneath the exhaustion to come to life.

TOOLS AND RESOURCES

Early Sleep Cues

△ The seven-mile stare/zoning out

△ Clinginess

△ Resting their head on your shoulder

△ Wants to be picked up but then doesn't

△ Back arching

△ Restlessness

△ Rooting (this is often perceived as hunger when it can sometimes be a sleep cue if feeding is a pre-sleep comfort for your baby)

△ Rubbing eyes (this can be a sign of a milk allergy or intolerance)

△ Fussy at the breast

△ Tired eyes

Late Sleep Cues:

△ All of the above

△ Yawning

△ Hair-pulling

△ Bobbing or dipped head

△ Crying

△ Screaming

△ Frustration

△ Anger

△ Frustration or agitation

△ Inability to settle once in cot

Your whys

To us, knowing our whys – the reason that we do the work we do with such fervour and passion – is essential to keeping us on track and in touch with our core purpose. Many parents find it helpful to identify the whys that resonate most deeply with them. Below you'll find our checklist for you to tick off and refer to as a reminder throughout the difficult times in your sleep journey.

I am choosing to enable solid sleep to:

☐ benefit my child's health and happiness

☐ teach my child the life-skill of peaceful settling

☐ help my child reach their developmental milestones

☐ make sure they can live their life to the fullest

☐ feel closer to them and enjoy them more

☐ feel more connected to my partner

☐ feel more patient and calmer

☐ have more clarity of mind

☐ boost my mental health

☐ enjoy our precious and fleeting time together

☐ make healthier life choices

☐ be less snappy/angry/resentful/despairing

☐ feel more present in the moment

☐ create time to do the things I love/that make me feel happy and fulfilled

☐ to be the parent I always dreamed of being

☐ have my evenings back

☐ be able to go out for an evening/day/night

☐ drink a hot cup of tea

☐ be free of anxiety and worry surrounding sleep

☐ feel more confident and empowered as a parent

Affirmations

△ I recognise and respect sleep as a key, fundamental, human need

△ I am worthy of rest and the healthy body and mind that it brings

△ I can only take care of others if I first take care of myself

△ I am perfectly capable of enabling best possible sleep

△ I am the best parent in the whole world for my child

△ I trust that I know what is right for my child and me

△ I am taking positive action to change my family's life for the better

△ I am enabling and empowering my baby with the life-skill of self-settling

△ I am ready to embrace the healing that solid sleep will bring

The exhaustion scale

We hope you find our exhaustion scale a useful start point to help you to think about whether sleep is working for you. Keep a note of your scores as you go.

In the last month, how often have you:

Felt rested and energised

Most of the time	4
Some of the time	3
Rarely	2
Not at all	1

Woken in the morning feeling positive, ready to embrace the day

Most of the time	4
Some of the time	3
Rarely	2
Not at all	1

Dreaded the night

Most of the time	1
Some of the time	2
Rarely	3
Not at all	4

Battled with sleep on some level

Most of the time	1
Some of the time	2
Rarely	3
Not at all	4

Been so tired you have cried, shouted or raged

Most of the time	1
Some of the time	2
Rarely	3
Not at all	4

Felt like you are not safe to drive

Most of the time 1
Some of the time 2
Rarely 3
Not at all 4

Felt so tired that you have had strong feelings of overwhelm or dread

Most of the time 1
Some of the time 2
Rarely 3
Not at all 4

Felt so tired that it negatively affects your life

Most of the time 1
Some of the time 2
Rarely 3
Not at all 4

Experienced intrusive thoughts or feelings due to exhaustion

Most of the time 1
Some of the time 2
Rarely 3
Not at all 4

Thought that you would give/do anything for a full night of sleep

Most of the time 1
Some of the time 2
Rarely 3
Not at all 4

30 or above – sleep is at a healthy level
20 or above – you may wish to consider seeking professional support
15 or below – it is strongly recommended that you seek professional support as soon as possible for the physical and mental well-being of your family

Scale created by Eve Squires, with references to the Edinburgh Post Natal Depression Scale

Eve's Poem, 'Untangled'

(A poem for parents)

You arrive in a torrent of overpowering love
Great waves crashing down on me
Waves of pride, of animalistic protectiveness
Waves of fear and anxiety
Echoed with my own experiences of childhood
But I am deaf to them

I hold your tiny hand
The most natural and yet most foreign thing in the world
How will I cope?
I will. I must.
The responsibility
The pressure
The honour

As you grow, I battle with myself
With the conflicting parenting advice
Pick the cherries, they say, but I do not know which ones
Too much love will spoil, too little will damage
The mountain of books towers over me, mocking me
Which way is the right way?

I am your world
Your need for me eclipses everything
I am needed, wanted, loved
I bask in the warmth of your need for me
It liberates and suffocates me
I snort you in
It is addictive
This love

When you need me
I comfort you
The only way I know how
Your needs and mine intermix, inextricably tangled together
You stifle under my efforts to parent you
I try to pull away
To let you grow
To give you space
It frightens me

And then it is time
For you to grow away from me a little
To sleep without me, outside of my arms
It's for the best they say
The first small step on the path of separation

I allow you to cry a little
The fear of your needs neglected claws away at me
You will need me
And I will not come
And then I will not be needed
Having broken my newborn promises to you
I crumble under their weight

Then a ray of clarity seers through the mist of a sleepless life
You begin to sleep yourself
And I realise
You still need me!
I am still your world
I have only given you the tools to do it yourself
I have empowered you
I have kept my promises

And so I make you a new promise
I will strive to separate your needs from mine
To untangle the roots of our needs, however deep
To equip you with the tools you need to fathom life
To send you out into the world
A soldier armed with love and compassion

I will let you go to keep you close
I will set you free to fly near me
I will swim above the waves of my love for you
Not drowning but swimming
Gliding
Breathing
Seeing
And you will swim alongside me too
Because I have taught you too
Because I love you.

Dedicated to Rachel & Ethan, C&B's first ever family.

FURTHER READING AND INFORMATION

The best way to reach our team is to email us on:
support@calmandbright.co.uk
Or send us a direct message on Instagram:
@calmandbrightsleepsupport.
We always have listening ears and open arms.

Maternal mental health signposting

Action on Postpartum Psychosis (APP)
Email: app@app-network.org

Association for Postnatal Illness
Helpline: 10 a.m. to 2 p.m.; 0207 386 0868
Email: info@apni.org

Best Beginnings
Free NHS-accredited Baby Buddy app offering evidence-based
information and self-care tools to help parents during pregnancy
and early stages of parenting.
App users also have access to a confidential, text-based Crisis
Messenger which provides 24/7 support for new and expectant
parents who are feeling extremely anxious or overwhelmed.

Maternal OCD
Peer support available
Email info@maternalocd.org to arrange

PANDAS

PANDAS is the UK's leading charity and support service for perinatal mental health. Free helpline open from 9 a.m. to 8 p.m. every day; 0808 1961 776
Email support available: info@pandasfoundation.org.uk
Web: pandasfoundation.org.uk/how-we-can-support-you/

Petals

Petals offers free-of-charge specialist counselling to anyone who has experienced pregnancy or baby loss.
Web: petalscharity.org/counsellingcontact/
Email: counselling@petalscharity.org
Tel: 0300 688 0068

Samaritans

Tel: 116 123 (this is a free telephone number and will not appear on the phone bill)
Web: www.samaritans.org
Email: jo@samaritans.org

Twins Trust

Twinline is Twins Trust's listening service for parents of twins, triplets and more. All the calls are answered by volunteers who have multiples themselves. Twinline is open Monday to Friday 10 a.m. to 1 p.m. and from 7 p.m. to 10 p.m. 0800 138 0509, alternatively email asktwinline@twinstrust.org.
Web: twinstrust.org/let-us-help/support/twinline.html

Tommy's

Tommy's has a team of in-house midwives who offer free support and information for women and their families at any stage of pregnancy and after the birth.
Free helpline open 9 a.m. to 5 p.m., Monday to Friday; 0800 014 7800
Web: www.tommys.org
Their midwives also answer questions via email, Facebook, Instagram and Twitter.
Email: midwife@tommys.org

NOTES

1 Mindell, Jodi A. PhD, Associate Director of the Sleep Center at the Children's Hospital of Philadelphia and author of *Sleeping Through the Night: How Infants, Toddlers, and Their Parents Can Get a Good Night's Sleep.*

2 Middlemiss, W., et al. (2012). Asynchrony of mother-infant hypo thalamic-pituitary-adrenal axis following extinction of infant crying responses induced during the transition to sleep. *Early Human Development*, 88(4), 227–232

3 www.theguardian.com/news/2014/dec/10/-sp-ceausescus-children

4 news.bbc.co.uk/1/hi/8425001.stm

5 www.kcl.ac.uk/news/spotlight/romanian-orphans-landmark-study-tracks-mental-health-27-years-later

6 Mackes, N.K. et al. (2020). Early childhood deprivation is associated with alterations in adult brain structure despite subsequent environmental enrichment. *Proceedings of the National Academy of Sciences of the United States of America*, 117(1), 641–649

7 Mindell J.A., et al. (2006). Behavioral treatment of bedtime problems and night wakings in infants and young children. *Sleep*, 29(10), 1263–1276

8 Everson, C.A., Bergmann, B.M. & Rechtschaffen, A. (1989). Sleep deprivation in the rat: III. Total sleep deprivation. *Sleep*, 12(1), 13–21.

9 Walker, Matthew (2018). *Why We Sleep*. Penguin Ltd, London

10 Ibid.

11 Fritschi, L. (2009). Shift work and cancer. *BMJ*; 339, b2653

12 www.med.stanford.edu/news/all-news/2017/06/sleep-disturbances-predict-increased-risk-for-suicidal-symptoms.html

13 Mitler, M.M., et al. (1988). Catastrophes, Sleep, and Public Policy: Consensus Report. *Sleep*, 11(1), 100–109

14 www.nih.gov/news-events/news-releases/brain-may-flush-out-toxins-during-sleep

15 www.mentalhealth.org.uk/sites/default/files/MHF-Sleep-Report-2011.pdf

16 www.ninds.nih.gov/Disorders/Patient-Caregiver-Education/Understanding-Sleep

17 Tefft, B.C. (2016). Acute Sleep Deprivation and Risk of Motor Vehicle Crash Involvement. AAA Foundation for Traffic Safety.

18 Hiscock, H., et al. (2007). Improving Infant Sleep and Maternal Mental Health. *Arch Dis Child*, 92(11), 952–958

19 Leeson, R., et al. (1994). Management of infant sleep problems in a residential unit. *Childcare Health Dev*, 20(2), 89–100

20 Hiscock, H., et al. (2008). Long-term mother and child mental health effects of a population-based infant sleep intervention: cluster-randomized, controlled trial. *Pediatrics*, 122(3), e621–e627

21 Gradisar, M., et al. (2016). Behavioral interventions for infant sleep problems: A randomized controlled trial. *Pediatrics*, 24:e20151486.

22 Mindell J.A., et al. (2006). Behavioral treatment of bedtime problems and night wakings in infants and young children. *Sleep*, 29(10), 1263–1276

23 www.psychotherapynetworker.org/blog/details/617/the-one-thing-thats-missing-from-attachment-theory

24 Miller, J.M., et al. (2015). Evaluating maternal recovery from labor and delivery: bone and levator ani injuries. *American journal of obstetrics and gynecology*, 213(2), 188.e1–188.e11

25 Jiang, F. (2019). Sleep and Early Brain Development. *Annals of nutrition & metabolism*, 75 Suppl 1, 44–54

26 Spruyt, K., et al. (2008). Relationship between sleep/wake patterns, temperament and overall development in term infants over the first year of life. *Early human development*, 84(5), 289–296

27 Ibid.

28 https://www.mumsnet.com/articles/mumsnet-on-covid

29 www.tuc.org.uk/sites/default/files/2021-04/WorkingMums.pdf

30 www.lullabytrust.org.uk/professionals/statistics-on-sids/

31 www.simplypsychology.org/saul-mcleod.html

32 Main, M., Kaplan, N. & Cassidy, J. (1985). Security in Infancy, Childhood, and Adulthood: A Move to the Level of Representation. *Monographs of the Society for Research in Child Development*, 50(1/2), 66–104

33 Scher, A. (2008). Maternal separation anxiety as a regulator of infants' sleep. *Journal of Child Psychology and Psychiatry*, 49, 618–625

34 Goodlin-Jones, B.L., Eiben, L.A. & Anders, T. F. (1997). Maternal well-being and sleep–wake behaviors in infants: An intervention using maternal odor. *Infant Mental Health Journal*, 18(4), 378–393

35 Gelman, V.S. & King, N.J. (2011). Wellbeing of mothers with children exhibiting sleep disturbance. *Australian Journal of Pyschology*, 53(1), 18–22

36 Stern, D.N. (1985). *The Interpersonal World of the Infant*. Routledge, Oxfordshire

37 Armitage, R., et al. (2009) Early developmental changes in sleep in infants: the impact of maternal depression. *Sleep*, 32(5), 693–696

38 Cunningham, N., et al. (1987). Infant carrying, breast feeding, and mother-infant relations. *Lancet*, 1(8529), 379

39 Moore, T. & Ukco, L.E. (1957). Night waking in early infancy: I. *Arch Dis Child*, 32(164), 333–342

40 Pinilla, T. & Birch, L.L. (1993). Help me make it through the night: behavioral entrainment of breast-fed infants' sleep patterns. *Pediatrics*, 91(2), 436–444

41 Siegel, A. (2009). Children's Dreams and Nightmares: Emerging Trends in Research Dreaming. American Psychological Association; *Dreaming: Journal of the Association for the Study of Dreams*, 15(3), 147–154

42 Van Horn, N.L. & Street, M. (2021). Night Terrors. In: *StatPearls*. StatPearls Publishing, Florida

INDEX

ACKNOWLEDGEMENTS

To every family who ever let us in, thank you for trusting that we could lead you back to yourselves.

To our dear Mum, who never leaves us in doubt of her love and pride, thank you for instilling a limitless belief in ourselves. Dad, thank you for being a living embodiment of kindness and for loving us and our children without reserve. Somehow, you are always there. Thank you.

To our husbands, Darryl and James, thank you for holding the fort selflessly while we sneaked off to write and write and write. Without your love and support, our words would never have found their home in the pages of this book.

To our eight children, Tilly, Finley, Toby, Sena, Louis, Ted, Kit and Posie, you force us every day to love ourselves better. May we always see ourselves as you see us.

To the outstanding women on the C&B team: Jenny, Lucy, Abbey, Laura and Beth. Thank you for holding us up and keeping our feet on the ground. Thank you for knowing the song in our hearts and singing it back to us when we've forgotten the words.

Thank you to all the people who gave their permission for their story or opinion to be in this book in the hope that it would help or inspire others.

To the Orion super team and our lush agent Hannah, thank you for helping us to believe that our message was one that the tired parents of the world needed to hear. We never expected anyone to be as excited about the book as we were, but you managed it somehow!

Lastly, we want to thank you, the reader of this book. In bravely seeking out our words, you have created a golden opportunity for sleep to find its way into your life. May it heal and nourish you and your loved ones forevermore.

ABOUT THE AUTHORS

Calm & Bright was born in 2009 when an exhausted first-time-mum had a minor crash while her baby was in the car. Eve's ten-month-old baby was waking every two hours overnight and her physical and mental health were deteriorating. Faced with two options – brutal sleep training, or the brutality of carrying on as she was – Eve developed her own peaceful pathway to a full night's sleep. Within three days of using her love-led, intuitive approach, her baby was sleeping 11–12 hours a night and life was transformed beyond measure. Compelled to help others, Eve volunteered her support to local families, until she could no longer meet demand. In 2014, Eve's sister Gem (a paediatric nurse of twenty years) joined the fold. Today, alongside their highly-qualified team of paediatric nurses and mental health professionals, the sisters have helped thousands of families around the world discover a life with sleep. Best known for their judgement-free approach, random acts of kindness and astonishing results, Eve and Gem have fast become a leading voice in early years sleep. In the last twelve months, their Instagram page has organically grown by 30,000 followers. Happy clients include Izzy Judd, Aston Merrygold, Rachaele Hambleton (Part-Time Working Mummy), psychotherapist Anna Mathur and Heart FM's Zoe Hardman.

Help us make the next generation of readers

We – both author and publisher – hope you enjoyed this book. We believe that you can become a reader at any time in your life, but we'd love your help to give the next generation a head start.

Did you know that 9 per cent of children don't have a book of their own in their home, rising to 13 per cent in disadvantaged families*? We'd like to try to change that by asking you to consider the role you could play in helping to build readers of the future.

We'd love you to think of sharing, borrowing, reading, buying or talking about a book with a child in your life and spreading the love of reading. We want to make sure the next generation continue to have access to books, wherever they come from.

And if you would like to consider donating to charities that help fund literacy projects, find out more at **www.literacytrust.org.uk** and **www.booktrust.org.uk**.

THANK YOU

*As reported by the National Literacy Trust